Selected Lab Exercises from

Laboratory Manual

tenth edition

Biology

Richard J. Daley College

Sylvia S. Mader

Mc
Graw
Hill
Education

14 15 16 17 FRD FRD 16 15 14

ISBN-13: 978-0-07-735871-6
ISBN-10: 0-07-735871-6

Learning Solutions Specialist: Tom Weitz
Project Manager: Sue Culbertson

Contents

Preface

To the Instructor

The laboratory exercises in this manual are coordinated with *Biology*, a general biology text that covers the entire field of biology from an evolutionary perspective.

Although each laboratory is referenced to the appropriate chapter(s) in *Biology*, this manual may also be used in coordination with other general biology texts. In addition, this laboratory manual can be adapted to a variety of course orientations and designs. There are a sufficient number of laboratories and exercises within each lab to tailor the laboratory experience as desired. Then, too, many exercises may be performed as demonstrations rather than as student activities, thereby shortening the time required to cover a particular concept.

The Exercises

All exercises have been tested for student interest, preparation time, time of completion, and feasibility. The following features are particularly appreciated by adopters:

Integrated opening: Each laboratory begins with a list of Learning Outcomes organized according to the major sections of the laboratory. The major sections of the laboratory are numbered on the opening page and in the laboratory text material. This organization will help students better understand the goals of each laboratory session.

Self-contained content: Each laboratory contains all the background information necessary to understand the concepts being studied and to answer the questions asked. This feature will reduce student frustration and increase learning.

Scientific process: All laboratories stress the scientific process, and many opportunities are given for students to gain an appreciation of the scientific method. The first laboratory of this edition explicitly explains the steps of the scientific method and gives students an opportunity to use them. I particularly recommend this laboratory because it utilizes the pillbug, a living subject.

Student activities: A color bar is used to designate each student activity. Some student exercises are Observations and some are Experimental Procedures. An icon appears whenever a procedure requires a period of time before results can be viewed. Sequentially numbered steps guide students as they perform each activity.

Live materials: Although students work with living material during some part of almost all laboratories, the exercises are designed to be completed within one laboratory session. This facilitates the use of the manual in multiple-section courses.

Laboratory safety: Laboratory safety is of prime importance, and the listing on page viii will assist instructors in making the laboratory experience a safe one.

Improvements in This Edition

All laboratories have been revised to:

1. Increase student participation by improving the learning outcomes and by applying the scientific method to many laboratory procedures. Students are invited to hypothesize the outcome of procedures; an improved wrap-up is provided so that students can come to a conclusion based on the results.

2. Increase relevancy by including applications of interest to students. For example, in Laboratory 4 students test various over-the-counter antacids for their ability to buffer HCl, and in Laboratory 5 the poisonous nature of hydrogen peroxide and the need for catalase activity in cells is exemplified by picturing a product utilizing hydrogen peroxide as an everyday antiseptic.

I am pleased to report that the following laboratories have been extensively revised:

Laboratory 3: Chemical Composition of Cells
   Increased student involvement allows students to independently carry out testing the chemical composition of everyday materials and an unknown.

Laboratory 6: Photosynthesis
   Utilization of the scientific method results in student appreciation of pigment utilization by plants to increase primary productivity. A new interactive section allows students to summarize the process of photosynthesis in a chloroplast.

Laboratory 7: Cellular Respiration
   Utilization of the scientific method and appropriate illustrations increases relevancy and student participation in a laboratory that contrasts fermentation with cellular respiration.

Laboratory 10: Human Genetics
   This population lab has been enhanced by a reorganization that allowed additional genetics problems, including an interactive exercise that helps students construct a pedigree.

Laboratory 12: Evidences of Evolution
   A new section on the geologic timescale precedes an examination of fossils that focuses on student observational skills. The comparison of chimpanzee and human skeletons was rewritten to include additional questions, conclusions, and art. A new interactive summary asks students to come to conclusions about the evidences of evolution.

Laboratory 16: Nonvascular Plants and Seedless Vascular Plants
   This lab now reflects the latest understanding of plant evolution and includes an observation of *Chara* as the living alga most closely related to land plants and lycophytes as respresentative of the first plants to have vascular tissue.

Laboratory 21: Reproduction in Flowering Plants
   A new interactive examination of the flowering plant life cycle leads to an appreciation of the role of pollinators and coevolution in the success of flowering plants. Observation of fruits has been simplified in order to give students an opportunity to better appreciate the role of fruits in the plant life cycle.

Laboratory 22: Introduction to Invertebrates
   Walks students through the modern phylogenetic tree of animal evolution based on molecular data. The lab also now gives students the opportunity to make their own observations of the noncoelomate invertebrates, such as living hydra and planarian, and report their findings.

Laboratory 29: Homeostasis
   Reorganization has sharpened the focus of this lab on homeostasis, including the contribution of certain organs such as the liver and kidneys whose activities are under hormonal control.

Laboratory 34: Sampling Ecosystems
   This lab was rewritten to make a field experience more enjoyable and practical for both the instructor and students.

Customized Editions

The 35 laboratories in this manual are now available as individual "lab separates," so instructors can custom-tailor the manual to their particular course needs.

Laboratory Resource Guide

The *Laboratory Resource Guide,* an essential aid for instructors and laboratory assistants, free to adopters of the *Laboratory Manual,* is online at www.mhhe.com/maderbiology10. The answers to the Laboratory Review questions are in the *Resource Guide.*

To the Student

Special care has been taken in preparing the *Biology Laboratory Manual* to enable you to **enjoy** the laboratory experience as you **learn** from it. The instructions and discussions are written clearly so that you can understand the material while working through it. Student aids are designed to help you focus on important aspects of each exercise.

Student Learning Aids

Student learning aids are carefully integrated throughout this manual. The Learning Outcomes set the goals of each laboratory session and help you review the material for a laboratory practical or any other kind of exam. The major sections of each laboratory are numbered, and the Learning Outcomes are grouped according to these topics. This system allows you to study the chapter in terms of the outcomes presented.

The Introduction reviews much of the necessary background information required for comprehending upcoming experiments. Color bars bring attention to exercises that require your active participation by highlighting Observations and Experimental Procedures, and an icon indicates a timed experiment. Throughout, space is provided for recording answers to questions and the results of investigations and experiments. Each laboratory ends with a set of review questions covering the day's work.

Appendices at the end of the book provide useful information on preparing a laboratory report, the metric system, and the Tree of Life. Practical examination answer sheets are also provided on the website.

Laboratory Preparation

Read each exercise before coming to the laboratory. *Study* the introductory material and the procedures. If necessary, to obtain a better understanding, read the corresponding chapter in your text. If your text is *Biology,* by Sylvia S. Mader, see the "text chapter reference" column in the table of contents at the beginning of the *Laboratory Manual.*

Explanations and Conclusions

Throughout a laboratory, you are often asked to formulate explanations or conclusions. To do so, you will need to synthesize information from a variety of sources, including the following:

1. Your experimental results and/or the results of other groups in the class. If your data are different from those of other groups in your class, do not erase your answer; add the other answers in parentheses.
2. Your knowledge of underlying principles. Obtain this information from the laboratory Introduction or the appropriate section of the laboratory and from the corresponding chapter of your text.
3. Your understanding of how the experiment was conducted and/or the materials used. *Note:* Ingredients can be contaminated or procedures incorrectly followed, resulting in reactions that seem inappropriate. If this occurs, consult with other students and your instructor to see if you should repeat the experiment.

In the end, be sure you are truly writing an explanation or conclusion and not just restating the observations made.

Color Bar and Icon

Throughout each laboratory, a color bar designates either an Observation or an Experimental Procedure.

Observation: An activity in which models, slides, and preserved or live organisms are observed to achieve a learning outcome.

Experimental Procedure: An activity in which a series of steps uses laboratory equipment to gather data and come to a conclusion.

Time: An icon is used to designate when time is needed for an Experimental Procedure. Allow the designated amount of time for this activity. Start these activities at the beginning of the laboratory, proceed to other activities, and return to these when the designated time is up.

Laboratory Review

Each laboratory ends with a number of thought questions that will help you determine whether you have accomplished the outcomes for the laboratory.

Student Feedback

If you have any suggestions for how this laboratory manual could be improved, you can send your comments to:

The McGraw-Hill Companies
Product Development—General Biology
501 Bell St.
Dubuque, Iowa 52001

Acknowledgments

We gratefully acknowledge the following for their assistance in the development of this lab manual:

Mark G. Birchette
Long Island University

Benjie Blair
Jacksonville State University

Raymond A. Burton
Germanna Community College

Paul Decelles
Johnson County Community College

Karen L. Dunston
San Jacinto College South

Julie Fischer
Wallace Community College—Dothan

Donald P. French
Oklahoma State University

Melanie A. Glasscock
Wallace State Community College

Andrew Goliszek
North Carolina A&T State University

Lula Gordon
Wayne County Community College

Chris Haynes
Shelton State Community College

Meg Horton
UNC—Greensboro

Gerald Sumners
University of Missouri

Michelle Tremblay
Georgia Southern University

Emily R. Watkinson
Virginia Commonwealth University

Laboratory Safety

The following is a list of practices required for safety purposes in the biology laboratory and in outdoor activities. Following rules of lab safety and using common sense throughout the course will enhance your learning experience by increasing your confidence in your ability to safely use chemicals and equipment. Pay particular attention to oral and written safety instructions given by the instructor. If you do not understand a procedure, ask the instructor, rather than a fellow student, for clarification. Be aware of your school's policy regarding accident liability and any medical care needed as a result of a laboratory or outdoor accident.

The following rules of laboratory safety should become a habit:

1. To prevent possible hazards to eyes or contact lenses, wear safety glasses or goggles during exercises in which glassware and solutions are heated, or when dangerous fumes may be present.
2. Assume that all reagents are poisonous and act accordingly. Read the labels on chemical bottles for safety precautions and know the nature of the chemical you are using. If chemicals come into contact with skin, wash immediately with water.
3. **DO NOT**
   a. ingest any reagents.
   b. eat, drink, or smoke in the laboratory. Toxic material may be present, and some chemicals are flammable.
   c. carry reagent bottles around the room.
   d. pipette anything by mouth.
   e. put chemicals in the sink or trash unless instructed to do so.
   f. pour chemicals back into containers unless instructed to do so.
   g. operate any equipment until you are instructed in its use.
4. **DO**
   a. note the location of emergency equipment such as a first aid kit, eyewash bottle, fire extinguisher, switch for ceiling showers, fire blanket(s), sand bucket, and telephone (911).
   b. become familiar with the experiments you will be doing before coming to the laboratory. This will increase your understanding, enjoyment, and safety during exercises. Confusion is dangerous. Completely follow the procedure set forth by the instructor.
   c. keep your work area neat, clean, and organized. Before beginning, remove everything from your work area except the lab manual, pen, and equipment used for the experiment. Wash hands and desk area, including desk top and edge, before and after each experiment. Use clean glassware at the beginning of each exercise, and wash glassware at the end of each exercise or before leaving the laboratory.
   d. wear clothing that, if damaged, would not be a serious loss, or use aprons or laboratory coats, since chemicals may damage fabrics.
   e. wear shoes as protection against broken glass or spillage that may not have been adequately cleaned up.
   f. handle hot glassware with a test tube clamp or tongs. Use caution when using heat, especially when heating chemicals. Do not leave a flame unattended; do not light a Bunsen burner near a gas tank or cylinder; do not move a lit Bunsen burner; do keep long hair and loose clothing well away from the flame; do make certain gas jets are off when the Bunsen burner is not in use. Use proper ventilation and hoods when instructed.
   g. read chemical bottle labels; be aware of the hazards of all chemicals used. Know the safety precautions for each.
   h. stopper all reagent bottles when not in use. Immediately wash reagents off yourself and your clothing if they spill on you, and immediately inform the instructor. If you accidentally get any reagent in your mouth, rinse the mouth thoroughly, and immediately inform your instructor.
   i. use extra care and wear disposable gloves when working with glass tubing and when using dissection equipment (scalpels, knives, or razor blades), whether cutting or assisting.
   j. administer first aid immediately to clean, sterilize, and cover any scrapes, cuts, and burns where the skin is broken and/or where there may be bleeding. Wear bandages over open skin wounds.
   k. report all accidents to the instructor immediately, and ask your instructor for assistance in cleaning up broken glassware and spills.
   l. report to the instructor any condition that appears unsafe or hazardous.
   m. use caution during any outdoor activities. Watch for snakes, poisonous insects or spiders, stinging insects, poison oak, poison ivy, and so on. Be careful near water.

I understand the safety rules as presented. I agree to follow them and all other instructions given by the instructor.

Name _____   Date _____

Laboratory Class and Time: _____

1

Scientific Method

Learning Outcomes

Introduction

This laboratory will provide you with an opportunity to use the scientific method in the same manner as scientists. Scientists often begin by making observations about the subject of interest. Today our subject is the pillbug, *Armadillidium vulgare,** a type of crustacean that lives on land.

Pillbugs have overlapping "armored" plates that make them look like little armadillos. A pillbug can roll up into such a tight ball that its legs and head are no longer visible, earning it the nickname "roly-poly." They are commonly found in damp leaf litter, under rocks, and in basements or crawl spaces under houses. Pillbugs breathe by gills located on the underside of their bodies. The gills must be kept slightly moist, and that is why they are usually found in damp places.

Following an inactive winter, pillbugs mate in the spring. Several weeks later, the eggs hatch and remain for six weeks in a brood pouch on the underside of the female's body. Once they leave the pouch, they eat primarily dead organic matter, including decaying leaves. Therefore, they are easy to find and maintain in a moist terrarium with leaf litter, rocks, and wood chips. You are encouraged to collect some for your experiment. Since they live in the same locations as snakes, be careful when collecting them.

Pillbugs molt (shed the exoskeleton) four or five times. They have three body parts: head, thorax, and abdomen. However, they are dorsoventrally flattened and lack a carapace. They do have compound eyes and two pairs of antennae. Currently, it is believed that pillbugs do not transmit diseases, nor do they bite or sting.

Pillbugs on leaf

*The garden snail, *Helix aspersa,* or the earthworm, *Lumbricus terrestris,* can be substituted as desired.

1.1 Using the Scientific Method

Science differs from other human ways of knowing and learning by its process, which can be quite varied because it can be adjusted to where and how a study is being conducted. Still, the scientific process often involves the use of the scientific method. In today's laboratory, we will use the scientific method to come to a conclusion about certain aspects of pillbug behavior. As depicted in Figure 1.1, the scientific method involves making observations, formulating hypotheses, doing experiments, and coming to a conclusion. Many conclusions on the same topic allow scientists to develop a scientific theory.

Making observations As a first step in their study of a topic, scientists use all their senses and also instruments such as a microscope to make observations of the natural world. Observations can also include something you read, such as the introduction to this laboratory, or to learn more about pillbugs you could do a Google search of the Web or talk to someone who has worked with pillbugs for a long time. Scientists keep notes about their observations as you will when observing a pillbug. Why must a scientist begin by making observations? _____

Formulating a hypothesis Based on their observations, scientists come to a tentative explanation about what they are investigating. Having read about the habitat of a pillbug, you will predict whether a pillbug will be attracted toward or repelled by different substances, such as a dry powder or a fruit juice. Knowing how a pillbug reacts, you will predict whether it will not move, move toward, or move away from these substances. Now you can formulate a hypothesis, such as, "When presented with baking soda, a pillbug will not move at all." Why is a hypothesis called an "educated guess?" _____

_____

Testing your hypothesis After formulating a hypothesis, a scientist experimentally tests the hypothesis. A well-designed experiment must have a control and a sample or event that is not exposed to the testing procedure. If the control and the test produce the same results, either the procedure is flawed or the hypothesis is false. What is the purpose of a control?

_____

The results of your experiment are called **data.** Data are any factual information that comes to light because of your experiment or perhaps from further observations you have made. It is very important for scientists to keep accurate records of all their data. When another person repeats the exact same experiment, their data should be the same. Why must a scientist keep complete records of an experiment? _____

Conclusion The data will either support or not support the hypothesis. For example, if you have hypothesized that a pillbug will not move when presented with baking soda and it does move, your hypothesis must be rejected. If a pillbug does not move, it means your hypothesis has been supported—and not that the hypothesis is true. After all, an instrument might be found that might detect an infinitesimal movement of a pillbug. Why don't scientists say they have proven their hypothesis true?

_____

Theory A "theory" in science is an encompassing conclusion based on many individual conclusions in the same field. For example, the cell theory states that all organisms are composed of cells. The cell theory is based on observations made by many scientists who, over many years, have observed a countless variety of living things. Obviously, we will not be developing any theories today.

How is a scientific theory different from a conclusion? _____

Figure 1.1 Flow diagram for the scientific method.
In general, scientists use this methodology to come to conclusions and develop theories about the natural world. The return arrow shows that scientists often choose to retest the same hypothesis or test a related hypothesis before arriving at a conclusion. Many conclusions from many related experiments and observations allows scientists to develop a scientific theory.

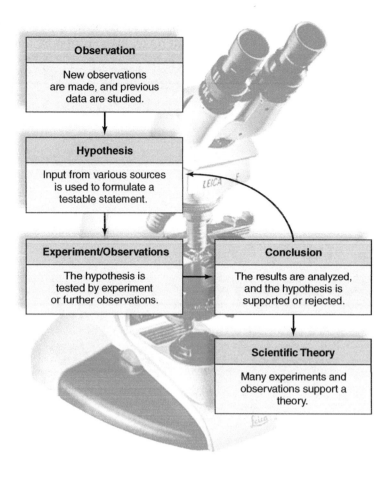

Observation
New observations are made, and previous data are studied.

Hypothesis
Input from various sources is used to formulate a testable statement.

Experiment/Observations
The hypothesis is tested by experiment or further observations.

Conclusion
The results are analyzed, and the hypothesis is supported or rejected.

Scientific Theory
Many experiments and observations support a theory.

1.2 Observing the Pillbug

Wash your hands before and after handling pillbugs. Please handle them carefully so they are not crushed. When touched, they roll up into a ball or "pill" shape as a defense mechanism. They will soon recover if left alone.

Observation: Pillbug's External Anatomy

1. Obtain a pillbug that has been numbered with white correction fluid or tape tags. First examine the shell and body with the unaided eye and then with a magnifying lens or dissecting microscope. Put the pillbug in a small glass or plastic dish to keep it contained.
2. Examine the shell shape, color, and texture.

   - Note the number of legs and antennae here._____
   - Are there any posterior appendages, such as uropods (paired appendages at end of abdomen) or brood pouches? (Females have leaflike growths at the base of some legs where developing eggs

     and embryos are held in pouches.) _____

   - Where are the eyes located?_____
   - Count the number of overlapping plates. _____

3. In the following space, draw a large outline of your pillbug (at least 10–12 cm across). Label the head, thorax, abdomen, antennae, eyes, uropods, and one of the seven pairs of legs.

4. Draw the pillbug rolled into a ball.

Observation: Pillbug's Motion

1. Watch a pillbug's underside as the pillbug moves up a transparent surface, such as the side of a graduated cylinder or beaker. Describe the action of the feet and any other motion you see.

_____

2. As you watch the pillbug, identify behaviors that might

   a. protect it from predators _____

   b. help it acquire food _____

   c. protect it from the elements _____

   d. allow interaction with the environment _____

3. Allow a pillbug to crawl on your hand. Describe how it feels and how it acts.

_____

4. Place the pillbug on a graduated cylinder. Experiment with the angle of the cylinder and the position of the pillbug to determine the pillbug's preferred direction of motion. For example, place the cylinder on end, and position the pillbug so that it can move up or down. Try other arrangements also. Repeat this procedure with three other pillbugs. Record the preferred direction of motion and other observations for each pillbug in Table 1.1.

Table 1.1 Preferred Direction of Motion		
Pillbug	**Direction Moved**	**Comments**
1		
2		
3		
4		

5. Measure the speed of the pillbug. Use what you learned about each pillbug's preferred direction of motion (see Table 1.1) to get maximum cooperation from each of the four pillbugs you worked with in step 4. Place each pillbug on a metric ruler, and use a stopwatch to measure the time it takes for the pillbug to move a certain number of centimeters. Record your results for each pillbug in Table 1.2. Calculate each pillbug's average speed in millimeters (mm) per second, and record your data in Table 1.2.

Table 1.2 Pillbug Speed			
Pillbug	**Millimeters Traveled**	**Time (sec)**	**Average Speed (mm/sec)**
1			
2			
3			
4			

1.3 Formulating Hypotheses

Hypotheses are often stated as "if-then" statements. For example, *if* the pillbug is exposed to _____, *then* it will be _____. You will be testing whether pillbugs are attracted to, repelled by, or unresponsive to particular substances. Pillbugs move away from a substance when they are repelled by it, and they move toward and eat a substance when they are attracted to it, and they do not move when they are unresponsive. If a pillbug simply rolls into a ball, nothing can be concluded, and you may wish to choose another pillbug or wait a minute or two to check for further response.

1. Choose
   a. two or three powders, such as flour, cornstarch, coffee creamer, baking soda, fine sand.
   b. two or three liquids, such as milk, orange juice, ketchup, applesauce, a carbonated beverage, water.
2. Hypothesize in Table 1.3 how you expect the pillbug to respond, and offer an explanation for your reasoning.

Table 1.3 Hypotheses About Pillbug's Reaction to Common Powders and Liquids		
Substance Tested	Hypothesis About How Pillbug Will Respond to Substance	Reasoning for Hypothesis
1		
2		
3		
4		
5		
6		

1.4 Performing an Experiment and Coming to a Conclusion

Design an experiment to test the pillbug's reaction to the chosen substances. The pillbug must be treated humanely. No substance must be put directly on the pillbug, nor can the pillbug be placed directly onto the substance. Since pillbugs tend to walk around the edge of a petri dish, you could put the wet or dry substance around the edge of the dish. Or for wet substances, you could put liquid-soaked cotton in the pillbug's path.

A good experimental design contains a **control.** A control group goes through all the steps of an experiment but lacks, or is not exposed to, the factor being tested. If you are testing the pillbug's reaction to a liquid, water can be the control substance substituted for the test liquid. If you are testing the pillbug's reaction to a powder, substitute fine sand for the test powder.

Experimental Procedure: Pillbug's Reaction to Common Substances

1. What substances are you testing? Include in your list any controls, and complete the first column in Table 1.4.
2. Obtain a small beaker and fill it with water. Rinse your pillbug between procedures by spritzing with distilled water from a spray bottle. Then put it on a paper towel to dry off.
3. Test the pillbug's reaction using the method described previously.

4. Watch the pillbug's reaction to each substance, and record it in Table 1.4.
5. Do your results support your hypotheses? Answer *yes* or *no* in the last column.

Table 1.4   Pillbug's Reaction to Common Substances

Substance Tested	Pillbug's Reaction	Hypothesis Supported?
1		
2		
3		
4		
5		
6		

6. Compare your results with those of other students who tested the same substances. Complete Table 1.5.

Table 1.5   Class Results

Group No.	Exp. 1 Direction	Exp. 2 Speed (mm/sec)	Exp. 3 Dry Control	Substances		Exp. 4 Wet Control	Substances	
1								
2								
3								
4								
5								
6								
7								
8								

Continuing the Experiment

7. Study your results and those of other students, and decide what factors may have caused the pillbug to be attracted to or repelled by a substance. _____

_____

On the basis of your decision, what is your new hypothesis? _____

_____

8. Test your hypothesis, and describe your results here. If possible, make a table to display your results.

9. Based on your new data, what is your conclusion?

Laboratory Review 1

1. What are the essential steps of the scientific method?

2. What is a hypothesis?

3. Is it sufficient to do a single experiment to test a hypothesis—why or why not?

4. What do you call a sample that goes through all the steps of an experiment but does not contain the factor being tested?

5. What part of a pillbug is for protection, and what does it do to protect itself?

6. Name one observation that you used to formulate your hypotheses regarding pillbug reactions toward various substances.

7. Why is it important to test one substance at a time when doing an experiment?

Indicate whether statements 8 and 9 are hypotheses, conclusions, or theories.

8. The data show that vaccines protect people from disease. _____

9. All living things are made of cells. _____

Biology Website

The companion website for *Biology* provides a wealth of information organized and integrated by chapter. You will find practice tests, animations, videos, and much more that will complement your learning and understanding of general biology.

www.mhhe.com/maderbiology10

McGraw-Hill Access Science Website

An Encyclopedia of Science and Technology Online which provides more information including videos that can enhance the laboratory experience.

www.accessscience.com

2

Metric Measurement and Microscopy

Learning Outcomes

2.1 The Metric System
- Use metric units of measurement for length, weight, volume, and temperature.   10–13

2.2 Microscopy
- Describe similarities and differences between the stereomicroscope (dissecting microscope), compound light microscope, and the electron microscope.   14–15

2.3 Stereomicroscope (Dissecting Microscope)
- Identify the parts and tell how to focus the stereomicroscope.   15–17

2.4 Use of the Compound Light Microscope
- Identify and give the function of the basic parts of the compound light microscope.   17–19
- List, in proper order, the steps for bringing an object into focus with the compound light microscope.   19–20
- Describe how the image is inverted by the compound light microscope.   20
- Calculate the total magnification and the diameter of field for both low- and high-power lens systems.   20–21
- Explain how a slide of colored threads provides information on the depth of field.   22

2.5 Microscopic Observations
- Name and describe the three kinds of cells studied in this exercise.   23–25
- State two differences between human epithelial cells and onion epidermal cells.   23–24
- Examine a wet mount of *Euglena* and pond water. Contrast the organisms observed in pond water.   25

Introduction

This laboratory introduces you to the metric system, which biologists use to indicate the sizes of cells and cell structures. This laboratory also examines the features, functions, and use of the compound light microscope and the stereomicroscope (dissecting microscope). Transmission and scanning electron microscopes are explained, and micrographs produced using these microscopes appear throughout this lab manual. The stereomicroscope and the scanning electron microscope view the surface and/or the three-dimensional structure of an object. The compound light microscope and the transmission electron microscope can view only extremely thin sections of a specimen. If a subject was sectioned lengthwise for viewing, the interior of the projections at the top of the cell, called cilia, would appear in the micrograph. A lengthwise cut through any type of specimen is called a **longitudinal section (l.s.).** On the other hand, if the subject in Figure 2.1 was sectioned crosswise below the area of the cilia, you would see other portions of the interior of the subject. A crosswise cut through any type of specimen is called a **cross section (c.s.).**

Figure 2.1   Longitudinal and cross sections.
a. Transparent view of a cell. **b.** A longitudinal section would show the cilia at the top of the cell. **c.** A cross section shows only the interior where the cut is made.

a. Cell

b. Longitudinal section

c. Cross section

2.1 The Metric System

The **metric system** is the standard system of measurement in the sciences, including biology, chemistry, and physics. It has tremendous advantages because all conversions, whether for volume, mass (weight), or length, can be in units of ten. Refer to Appendix B, page 522, for an in-depth look at the units of the metric system.

Length

Metric units of length measurement include the **meter (m), centimeter (cm), millimeter (mm), micrometer (μm),** and **nanometer (nm)** (Table 2.1). The prefixes milli- (10^{-3}), micro- (10^{-6}), and nano (10^{-9}) are used with length, weight, and volume.

Table 2.1 Metric Units of Length Measurement				
Unit	Meters	Millimeters	Centimeters	Relative Size
Meter (m)	1 m	1,000 mm	100 cm	Largest
Centimeter (cm)	0.01 (10^{-2}) m	10 mm	1 cm	
Millimeter (mm)	0.001 (10^{-3}) m	1.0 mm	0.1 cm	
Micrometer (μm)	0.000001 (10^{-6}) m	0.001 (10^{-3}) mm	0.0001 (10^{-4}) cm	
Nanometer (nm)	0.000000001 (10^{-9}) m	0.000001 (10^{-6}) mm	0.0000001 (10^{-7}) cm	Smallest

Experimental Procedure: Length

1. Obtain a small ruler marked in centimeters and millimeters. How many centimeters are

   represented? _____ One centimeter equals how many millimeters? _____ To express

   the size of small objects, such as cell contents, biologists use even smaller units of the metric
   system than those on the ruler. These units are the micrometer (μm) and the nanometer (nm).

   According to Table 2.1, 1 μm = _____ mm, and 1 nm = _____ mm.

   Therefore, 1 mm = _____ μm = _____ nm.

2. Measure the diameter of the circle shown below to the nearest millimeter. This circle is

   _____ mm = _____ μm = _____ nm.

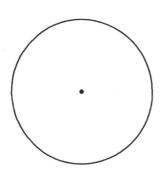

3. Obtain a meterstick. On one side, find the numbers 1 through 39, which denote inches. One meter equals 39.37 inches; therefore, 1 meter is roughly equivalent to 1 yard. Turn the meterstick over, and observe the metric subdivisions. How many centimeters are in a meter? _____ How many millimeters are in a meter? _____ The prefix *milli* means _____.

4. Use the meterstick and the method shown in Figure 2.2 to measure the length of two long bones from a disarticulated human skeleton. Lay the meterstick flat on the lab table. Place a long bone next to the meterstick between two pieces of cardboard (each about 10 cm × 30 cm), held upright at right angles to the stick. The narrow end of each piece of cardboard should touch the meterstick. The length between the cards is the length of the bone in centimeters. For example, if the bone measures from the 22 cm mark to the 50 cm mark, the length of the bone is _____ cm. If the bone measures from the 22 cm mark to midway between the 50 cm and 51 cm marks, its length is _____ mm, or _____ cm.

5. Record the length of two bones. First bone: _____ cm = _____ mm. Second bone: _____ cm = _____ mm.

Figure 2.2 Measurement of a long bone.
How to measure a long bone using a meterstick.

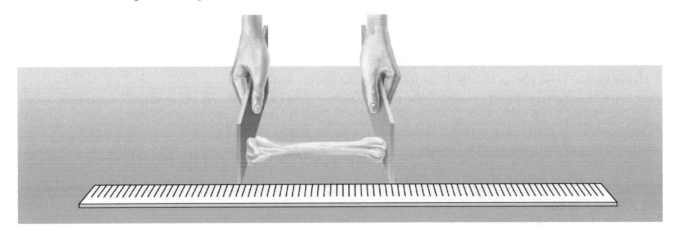

Weight

Two metric units of weight are the **gram (g)** and the **milligram (mg).** A paper clip weighs about 1 g, which equals 1,000 mg. 2 g = _____ mg; 0.2 g = _____ mg; and 2 mg = _____ g.

Experimental Procedure: Weight

1. Use a balance scale to measure the weight of a wooden block small enough to hold in the palm of your hand.

2. Measure the weight of the block to the tenth of a gram. The weight of the wooden block is _____ g = _____ mg.

3. Measure the weight of an item small enough to fit inside the opening of a 50 ml graduated cylinder. The item, a(n) _____, is _____ g = _____ mg.

Volume

Two metric units of volume are the **liter (l)** and the **milliliter (ml).** One liter = 1,000 ml.

Experimental Procedure: Volume

1. Volume measurements can be related to those of length. For example, use a millimeter ruler to measure the wooden block used in the previous Experimental Procedure to get its length, width, and depth.

   length = _____ cm; width = _____ cm; depth = _____ cm

   The volume, or space, occupied by the wooden block can be expressed in cubic centimeters (cc or cm^3) by multiplying: length × width × depth = _____ cm^3. For purposes of this Experimental Procedure, 1 cubic centimeter equals 1 milliliter; therefore, the wooden block has a volume of = _____ ml.

2. In the biology laboratory, liquid volume is usually measured directly in liters or milliliters with appropriate measuring devices. For example, use a 50 ml graduated cylinder to add 20 ml of water to a test tube. First, fill the graduated cylinder to the 20 ml mark. To do this properly, you have to make sure that the lowest margin of the water level, or the **meniscus** (Fig. 2.3), is at the 20 ml mark. Place your eye directly parallel to the level of the meniscus, and add water until the meniscus is at the 20 ml mark. (Having a dropper bottle filled with water on hand can help you do this.) A large, blank, white index card held behind the cylinder can also help you see the scale more clearly. Now pour the 20 ml of water into the test tube.

3. Hypothesize how you could find the total volume of the test tube. _____

   _____

   _____

   What is the test tube's total volume? _____

Figure 2.3   Meniscus.
The proper way to view the meniscus.

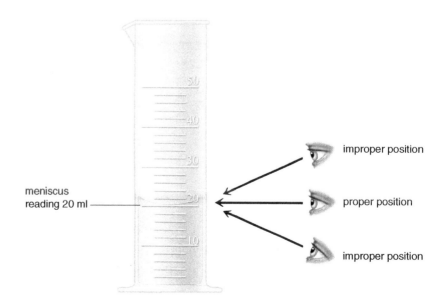

meniscus
reading 20 ml

improper position

proper position

improper position

4. Fill a 50 ml graduated cylinder with water to about the 20 ml mark. Hypothesize how you could use this setup to calculate the volume of an object. _____

_____

Now perform the operation you suggested. The object, _____, has a volume of _____ml.

5. Hypothesize how you could determine how many drops from the pipette of the dropper bottle equal 1 ml._____

Now perform the operation you suggested. How many drops from the pipette of the dropper bottle equal 1 ml? _____ Some pipettes are graduated and can be filled to a certain level as a way to measure volume directly. Your instructor will demonstrate this. Are pipettes customarily used to measure large or small volumes? _____

Temperature

There are two temperature scales: the **Fahrenheit (F)** and **Celsius (centigrade, C)** scales (Fig. 2.4). Scientists use the Celsius scale.

Experimental Procedure: Temperature

1. Study the two scales in Figure 2.4, and complete the following information:

    a. Water freezes at either _____ °F or _____ °C.

    b. Water boils at either _____ °F or _____ °C.

2. To convert from the Fahrenheit to the Celsius scale, use the following equation:

$$°C = (°F - 32°)/1.8$$
$$or$$
$$°F = (1.8°C) + 32$$

    Human body temperature of 98°F is what temperature on the Celsius scale? _____

3. Record any two of the following temperatures in your lab environment. In each case, allow the end bulb of the Celsius thermometer to remain in or on the sample for one minute.

    Room temperature = _____ °C

    Surface of your skin = _____ °C

    Cold tap water in a 50 ml beaker = _____ °C

    Hot tap water in a 50 ml beaker = _____ °C

    Ice water = _____ °C

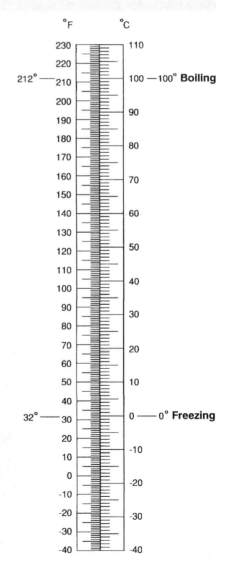

Figure 2.4 Temperature scales.
The Fahrenheit (°F) scale is on the left, and the Celsius (°C) scale is on the right.

2.2 Microscopy

Because biological objects can be very small, we often use a microscope to view them. Many kinds of instruments, ranging from the hand lens to the electron microscope, are effective magnifying devices. A short description of two kinds of light microscopes and two kinds of electron microscopes follows.

Light Microscopes

Light microscopes use light rays passing through lenses to magnify the object. The **stereomicroscope (dissecting microscope)** is designed to study entire objects in three dimensions at low magnification. The **compound light microscope** is used for examining small or thinly sliced sections of objects under higher magnification than that of the stereomicroscope. The term **compound** refers to the use of two sets of lenses: the ocular lenses located near the eyes and the objective lenses located near the object. Illumination is from below, and visible light passes through clear portions but does not pass through opaque portions. To improve contrast, the microscopist uses stains or dyes that bind to cellular structures and absorb light. Photomicrographs, also called light micrographs, are images produced by a compound light microscope (Fig. 2.5a).

Figure 2.5   Comparative micrographs.
Micrographs of a lymphocyte, a type of white blood cell. **a.** A photomicrograph (light micrograph) shows less detail than a **(b)** transmission electron micrograph (TEM). **c.** A scanning electron micrograph (SEM) shows the cell surface in three dimensions.

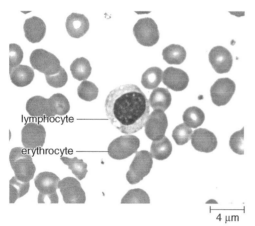

4 μm

a. Photomicrograph or light micrograph (LM)

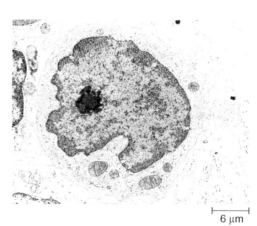

6 μm

b. Transmission electron micrograph (TEM)

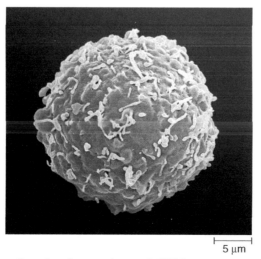

5 μm

c. Scanning electron micrograph (SEM)

Electron Microscopes

Electron microscopes use beams of electrons to magnify the object. The beams are focused on a photographic plate by means of electromagnets. The **transmission electron microscope** is analogous to the compound light microscope. The object is ultra-thinly sliced and treated with heavy metal salts to improve contrast. Figure 2.5*b* is a micrograph produced by this type of microscope. The **scanning electron microscope** is analogous to the dissecting light microscope. It gives an image of the surface and dimensions of an object, as is apparent from the scanning electron micrograph in Figure 2.5*c*.

The micrographs in Figure 2.5 demonstrate that an object is magnified more with an electron microscope than with a compound light microscope. The difference between these two types of microscopes, however, is not simply a matter of magnification; it is also the electron microscope's ability to show detail. The electron microscope has greater resolving power. **Resolution** is the minimum distance between two objects at which they can still be seen, or resolved, as two separate objects. The use of high-energy electrons rather than light gives electron microscopes a much greater resolving power since two objects that are much closer together can still be distinguished as separate points. Table 2.2 lists several other differences between the compound light microscope and the transmission electron microscope.

Table 2.2 Comparison of the Compound Light Microscope and the Transmission Electron Microscope	
Compound Light Microscope	**Transmission Electron Microscope**
1. Glass lenses	1. Electromagnetic lenses
2. Illumination by visible light	2. Illumination due to beam of electrons
3. Resolution $\cong$ 200 nm	3. Resolution $\cong$ 0.1 nm
4. Magnifies to 2,000×	4. Magnifies to 1,000,000×
5. Costs up to tens of thousands of dollars	5. Costs up to hundreds of thousands of dollars

Conclusions: Microscopy

- Which two types of microscopes view the surface of an object? _____
- Which two types of microscopes view objects that have been sliced and treated to improve contrast? _____
- Of the microscopes just mentioned, which one resolves the greater amount of detail?

2.3   Stereomicroscope (Dissecting Microscope)

The **stereomicroscope (dissecting microscope)** allows you to view objects in three dimensions at low magnifications. It is used to study entire small organisms, any object requiring lower magnification, and opaque objects that can be viewed only by reflected light. It is called a stereomicroscope because it produces a three-dimensional image.

Identifying the Parts

After your instructor has explained how to carry a microscope, obtain a stereomicroscope and a separate illuminator, if necessary, from the storage area. Place it securely on the table. Plug in the power cord, and turn on the illuminator. There is a wide variety of stereomicroscope styles, and your instructor will discuss the specific style(s) available to you. Regardless of style, the following features should be present:

1. **Binocular head:** Holds two eyepiece lenses that move to accommodate for the various distances between different individuals' eyes.
2. **Eyepiece lenses:** The two lenses located on the binocular head. What is the magnification of your eyepieces? _____ Some models have one **independent focusing eyepiece** with a knurled knob to allow independent adjustment of each eye. The nonadjustable eyepiece is called the **fixed eyepiece.**
3. **Focusing knob:** A large, black or gray knob located on the arm; used for changing the focus of both eyepieces together.

Figure 2.6   Stereomicroscope.
Label this stereomicroscope with the help of the text material.

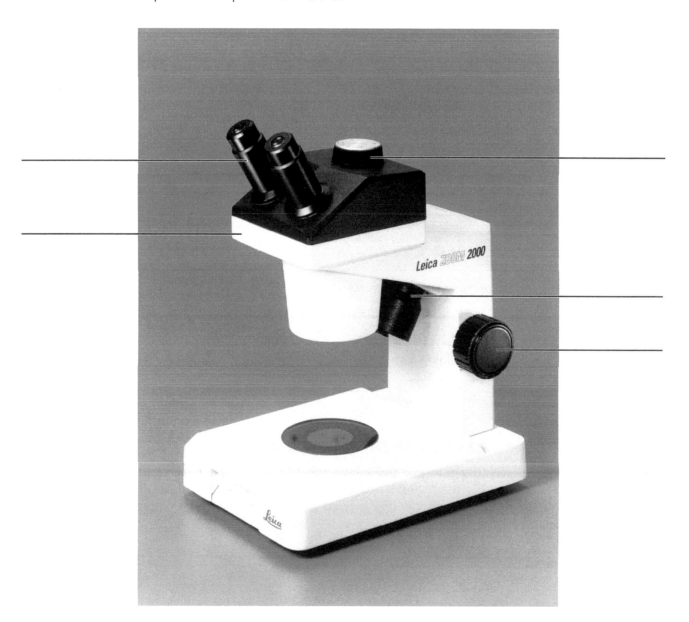

4. **Magnification changing knob:** A knob, often built into the binocular head, used to change magnification in both eyepieces simultaneously. This may be a **zoom** mechanism or a **rotating lens** mechanism of different powers that clicks into place.

5. **Illuminator:** Used to illuminate an object from above; may be built into the microscope or separate.

Locate each of these parts on your stereomicroscope, and label them on Figure 2.6.

Focusing the Stereomicroscope

1. In the center of the stage, place a plastomount that contains small organisms.

2. Adjust the distance between the eyepieces on the binocular head so that they comfortably fit the distance between your eyes. You should be able to see the object with both eyes as one three-dimensional image.

3. Use the focusing knob to bring the object into focus.

4. Does your microscope have an independent focusing eyepiece? _____ If so, use the focusing knob to bring the image in the fixed eyepiece into focus, while keeping the eye at the independent focusing eyepiece closed. Then adjust the independent focusing eyepiece so that the image is clear, while keeping the other eye closed. Is the image inverted? _____

5. Turn the magnification changing knob, and determine the kind of mechanism on your microscope. A zoom mechanism allows continuous viewing while changing the magnification. A rotating lens mechanism blocks the view of the object as the new lenses are rotated. Be sure to click each lens firmly into place. If you do not, the field will be only partially visible. What kind of mechanism is on your microscope? _____

6. Set the magnification changing knob on the lowest magnification. Sketch the object in the following circle as though this represents your entire field of view:

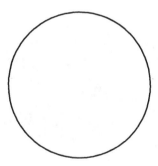

7. Rotate the magnification changing knob to the highest magnification. Draw another circle within the one provided to indicate the reduction of the field of view.

8. Experiment with various objects at various magnifications until you are comfortable with using the stereomicroscope.

2.4 Use of the Compound Light Microscope

As mentioned, the name **compound light microscope** indicates that it uses two sets of lenses and light to view an object. The two sets of lenses are the ocular lenses located near the eyes and the objective lenses located near the object. Illumination is from below, and the light passes through clear portions but does not pass through opaque portions. This microscope is used to examine small or thinly sliced sections of objects under higher magnification than would be possible with the stereomicroscope.

Identifying the Parts

Obtain a compound light microscope from the storage area, and place it securely on the table. *Identify the following parts on your microscope, and label them in Figure 2.7 with the help of the text material.*

Figure 2.7 Compound light microscope.
Compound light microscope with binocular head and mechanical stage.

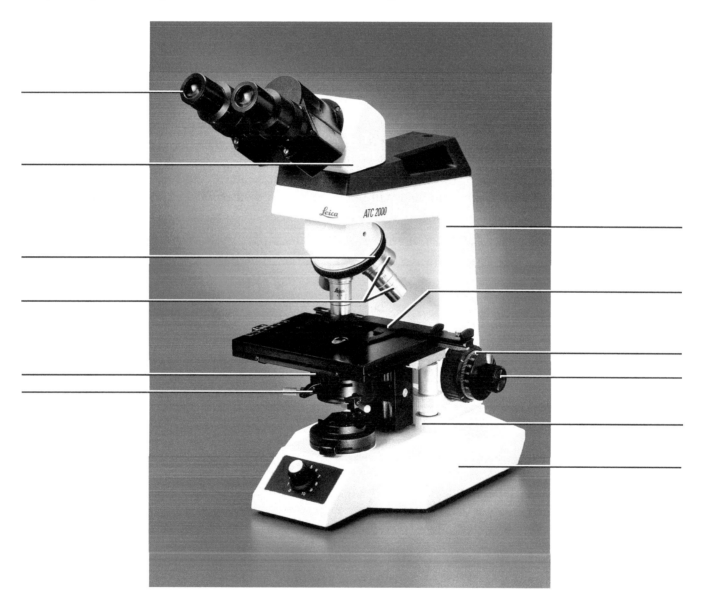

1. **Eyepieces** (ocular lenses): What is the magnifying power of the ocular lenses on your microscope? _____
2. **Viewing head:** Holds the ocular lenses.
3. **Arm:** Supports upper parts and provides carrying handle.
4. **Nosepiece:** Revolving device that holds objectives.

Rules for Microscope Use

Observe the following rules for using a microscope:

1. The lowest power objective (scanning or low) should be in position, both at the beginning and end of microscope use.
2. Use only lens paper for cleaning lenses.
3. Do not tilt the microscope as the eyepieces could fall out, or wet mounts could be ruined.
4. Keep the stage clean and dry to prevent rust and corrosion.
5. Do not remove parts of the microscope.
6. Keep the microscope dust-free by covering it after use.
7. Report any malfunctions.

5. **Objectives** (objective lenses):
   a. **Scanning objective:** This is the shortest of the objective lenses and is used to scan the whole slide. The magnification is stamped on the housing of the lens. It is a number followed by an ×. What is the magnifying power of the scanning objective lens on your microscope? _____

   b. **Low-power objective:** This lens is longer than the scanning objective lens and is used to view objects in greater detail. What is the magnifying power of the low-power objective lens on your microscope? _____

   c. **High-power objective:** If your microscope has three objective lenses, this lens will be the longest. It is used to view an object in even greater detail. What is the magnifying power of the high-power objective lens on your microscope? _____

   d. **Oil immersion objective:** (on microscopes with four objective lenses): Holds a 95× (to 100×) lens and is used in conjunction with immersion oil to view objects with the greatest magnification.

   Does your microscope have an oil immersion objective? _____ If this lens is available, your instructor will discuss its use when the lens is needed.

6. **Stage:** Holds and supports microscope slides. A mechanical stage is a movable stage that aids in the accurate positioning of the slide. Does your microscope have a mechanical stage? _____

7. **Coarse-adjustment knob:** Knob used to bring object into approximate focus; used only with low-power objective.

8. **Fine-adjustment knob:** Knob used to bring object into final focus.

9. **Condenser:** Lens system below the stage used to focus the beam of light on the object being viewed.

10. **Diaphragm** or **diaphragm control lever:** Controls amount of illumination used to view the object.

11. **Light source:** An attached lamp that directs a beam of light up through the object.

12. **Base:** The flat surface of the microscope that rests on the table.

Focusing the Compound Light Microscope—Lowest Power

1. Turn the nosepiece so that the *lowest* power objective on your microscope is in straight alignment over the stage.
2. Always begin focusing with the *lowest* power objective on your microscope (4× [scanning] or 10× [low power]).
3. With the coarse-adjustment knob, lower the stage (or raise the objectives) until it stops.
4. Place a slide of the letter *e* on the stage, and stabilize it with the clips. (If your microscope has a mechanical stage, pinch the spring of the slide arms on the stage, and insert the slide.) Center the *e* as best you can on the stage or use the two control knobs located below the stage (if your microscope has a mechanical stage) to center the *e*.

Laboratory 2   Metric Measurement and Microscopy   **19**

5. Again, be sure that the lowest-power objective is in place. Then, as you look from the side, decrease the distance between the stage and the tip of the objective lens until the lens comes to an automatic stop or is no closer than 3 mm above the slide.
6. While looking into the eyepiece, rotate the diaphragm (or diaphragm control lever) to give the maximum amount of light.
7. Using the coarse-adjustment knob, slowly increase the distance between the stage and the objective lens until the object—in this case, the letter *e*—comes into view, or focus.
8. Once the object is seen, you may need to adjust the amount of light. To increase or decrease the contrast, rotate the diaphragm slightly.
9. Use the fine-adjustment knob to sharpen the focus if necessary.
10. Practice having both eyes open when looking through the eyepiece, as this greatly reduces eyestrain.

Inversion

Inversion refers to the fact that a microscopic image is upside down and reversed.

Observation: Inversion

1. Draw the letter *e* as it appears on the slide (with the unaided eye, not looking through the eyepiece). _____

2. Draw the letter *e* as it appears when you look through the eyepiece. _____

3. What differences do you notice? _____

4. Move the slide to the right. Which way does the image appear to move? _____
   Explain. _____

Focusing the Compound Light Microscope—Higher Powers

Compound light microscopes are **parfocal;** that is, once the object is in focus with the lowest power, it should also be almost in focus with the higher power.

1. Bring the object into focus under the lowest power by following the instructions in the previous section.
2. Make sure that the letter *e* is centered in the field of the lowest objective.
3. Move to the next higher objective (low power [10×] or high power [40×]) by turning the nosepiece until you hear it click into place. Do not change the focus; parfocal microscope objectives will not hit normal slides when changing the focus if the lowest objective is initially in focus. (If you are on low power [10×], proceed to high power [40×] before going on to step 4.)
4. If any adjustment is needed, use only the *fine*-adjustment knob. (*Note:* Always use only the fine-adjustment knob with high power, and do not use the coarse-adjustment knob.)
5. On a drawing of the letter *e,* draw a circle around the portion of the letter that you are now seeing with high-power magnification. _____
6. When you have finished your observations of this slide (or any slide), rotate the nosepiece until the lowest-power objective clicks into place, and then remove the slide.

Total Magnification

Total magnification is calculated by multiplying the magnification of the ocular lens (eyepiece) by the magnification of the objective lens. The magnification of a lens is imprinted on the lens casing.

Observation: Total Magnification

Calculate total magnification figures for your microscope, and record your findings in Table 2.3.

Table 2.3 Total Magnification			
Objective	Ocular Lens	Objective Lens	Total Magnification
Scanning power (if present)			
Low power			
High power			
Oil immersion (if present)			

Field of View

A microscope's **field of view** is the circle visible through the lenses. The **diameter of field** is the length of the field from one edge to the other.

Observation: Field of View

Low-Power (10×) Diameter of Field

1. Place a clear, plastic ruler across the stage so that the edge of the ruler is visible as a horizontal line along the diameter of the low-power (not scanning) field. Be sure that you are looking at the millimeter side of the ruler.

2. Estimate the number of millimeters, to tenths, that you see along the field: _____ mm. (*Hint:* Start with one of the millimeter markers at the edge of the field.) Convert the figure to micrometers: _____ μm. This is the **low-power diameter of field (LPD)** for your microscope in micrometers.

High-Power (40×) Diameter of Field

1. To compute the **high-power diameter of field (HPD),** substitute these data into the formula given:

   a. LPD = low-power diameter of field (in micrometers) = _____

   b. LPM = low-power total magnification (from Table 2.3) = _____

   c. HPM = high-power total magnification (from Table 2.3) = _____

Example: If the diameter of field is about 2 mm, then the LPD is 2,000 μm. Using the LPM and HPM values from Table 2.3, the HPD would be 500 μm.

$$HPD = LPD \times \frac{LPM}{HPM}$$

$$HPD = (\quad) \times \frac{(\quad)}{(\quad)} = \underline{\quad\quad}$$

Conclusions: Total Magnification and Field of View

- Does low power or high power have a larger field of view (one that allows you to see more of the object)? _____

- Which has a smaller field but magnifies to a greater extent? _____

- To locate small objects on a slide, first find them under _____ ; then place them in the center of the field before rotating to _____.

Depth of Field

When viewing an object on a slide under high power, the **depth of field** (Fig. 2.8) is the area—from top to bottom—that comes into focus while slowly focusing up and down with the microscope's fine-adjustment knob.

Observation: Depth of Field

1. Obtain a prepared slide with three or four colored threads mounted together, or prepare a wet-mount slide with three or four crossing threads or hairs of different colors. (Directions for preparing a wet mount are given in Section 2.5.)
2. With low power, find a point where the threads or hairs cross. Slowly focus up and down. Notice that when one thread or hair is in focus, the others seem blurred. *Determine the order of the threads or hairs, and complete Table 2.4.* Remember, as the stage moves upward (or the objectives move downward), objects on top come into focus first.
3. Switch to high power, and notice that the depth of field is more shallow with high power than with low power. Constant use of the fine-adjustment knob when viewing a slide with high power will give you an idea of the specimen's three-dimensional form. For example, viewing a number of sections allows reconstruction of the three-dimensional structure, as demonstrated in Figure 2.10.

Figure 2.8 Depth of field.
A demonstration of how focusing at depths 1, 2, and 3 would produce three different images (views) that could be used to reconstruct the original three-dimensional structure of the object.

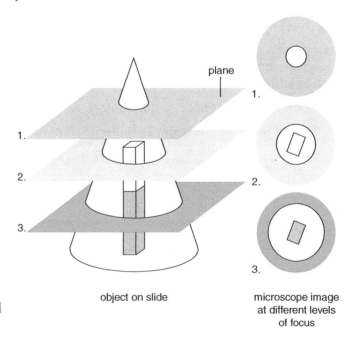

object on slide

microscope image at different levels of focus

Table 2.4 Order of Threads (or Hairs)	
Depth	**Thread (or Hair) Color**
Top	
Middle	
Bottom	

2.5 Microscopic Observations

When a specimen is prepared for observation, the object should always be viewed as a **wet mount**. A wet mount is prepared by placing a drop of liquid on a slide or, if the material is dry, by placing it directly on the slide and adding a drop of water or stain. The mount is then covered with a coverslip, as illustrated in Figure 2.9. Dry the bottom of your slide before placing it on the stage.

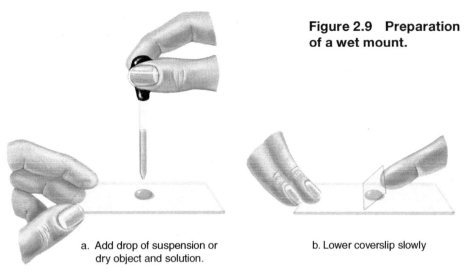

Figure 2.9 Preparation of a wet mount.

a. Add drop of suspension or dry object and solution.

b. Lower coverslip slowly

> ⚠️ **Methylene blue** Avoid ingestion, inhalation, and contact with skin, eyes, and mucous membranes. Exercise care in using this chemical. If any should spill on your skin, wash the area with mild soap and water. Methylene blue will also stain clothing. Follow your instructor's directions for its disposal.

Human Epithelial Cells

Epithelial cells cover the body's surface and line its cavities.

Observation: Human Epithelial Cells

1. Obtain a prepared slide, or make your own as follows:
   a. Obtain a prepackaged flat toothpick (or sanitize one with alcohol or alcohol swabs).
   b. Gently scrape the inside of your cheek with the toothpick, and place the scrapings on a clean, dry slide. Discard used toothpicks in the biohazard waste container provided.
   c. Add a drop of very weak *methylene blue* or *iodine solution,* and cover with a coverslip.
2. Observe under the microscope.
3. Locate the nucleus (the central, round body), the cytoplasm, and the plasma membrane (outer cell boundary). *Label Figure 2.10.*
4. Because your epithelial slides are biohazardous, they must be disposed of as indicated by your instructor.

Figure 2.10 Cheek epithelial cells.
Label the nucleus, the cytoplasm, and the plasma membrane.

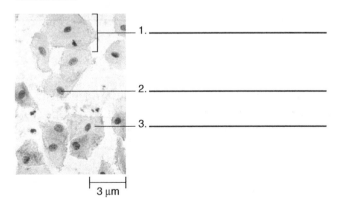

1. _____

2. _____

3. _____

3 µm

Onion Epidermal Cells

⚠️ **Scalpel** Exercise care when using a scalpel.

Epidermal cells cover the surfaces of plant organs, such as leaves. The bulb of an onion is made up of fleshy leaves.

Observation: Onion Epidermal Cells

1. With a scalpel, strip a small, thin, transparent layer of cells from the inside of a fresh onion leaf.
2. Place it gently on a clean, dry slide, and add a drop of *iodine solution* (or *methylene blue*). Cover with a coverslip.
3. Observe under the microscope.
4. Locate the cell wall and the nucleus. *Label Figure 2.11.*
5. Count the number of onion cells that line up end to end in a single line across the diameter of the high-power (40✕) field._____

   Based on what you learned in Section 2.4 about measuring diameter of field, what is your high-power diameter of field (HPD) in micrometers? _____ µm

   Calculate the length of each onion cell (HPD ÷ number of cells): _____ µm
6. Note some obvious differences between the human cheek cells and the onion cells, and list them in Table 2.5.

Figure 2.11   Onion epidermal cells.
Label the cell wall and the nucleus.

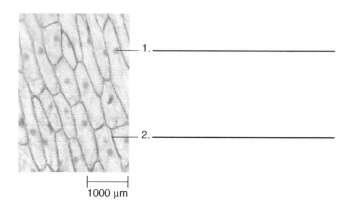

1._____

2._____

1000 µm

Table 2.5 Differences Between Human Epithelial and Onion Epidermal Cells		
Differences	**Human Epithelial Cells (Cheek)**	**Onion Epidermal Cells**

Euglena

Examination of *Euglena* (a unicellular organism with a flagellum to facilitate movement) will test your ability to observe objects with the microscope, to utilize depth of field, and to control illumination to heighten contrast.

Observation: Euglena

1. Make a wet mount of *Euglena* by using a drop of a *Euglena* culture and adding a drop of Protoslo® (methyl cellulose solution) onto a slide. The Protoslo® slows the organism's swimming.
2. Mix thoroughly with a toothpick, and add a coverslip.
3. Scan the slide for *Euglena:* Start at the upper left-hand corner, and move the slide forward and back as you work across the slide from left to right. The *Euglena* may be at the edge of the slide because they show an aversion to Protoslo®. Use Figure 2.12 to help identify the structural details of *Euglena.*
4. Experiment by using scanning, low-power, and high-power objective lenses; by focusing up and down with the fine-adjustment knob; and by adjusting the light so that it is not too bright.
5. Compare your *Euglena* specimens with Figure 2.12. List the labeled features that you can

    actually see: _____

    _____

Figure 2.12 *Euglena.*
Euglena is a unicellular, flagellated organism.

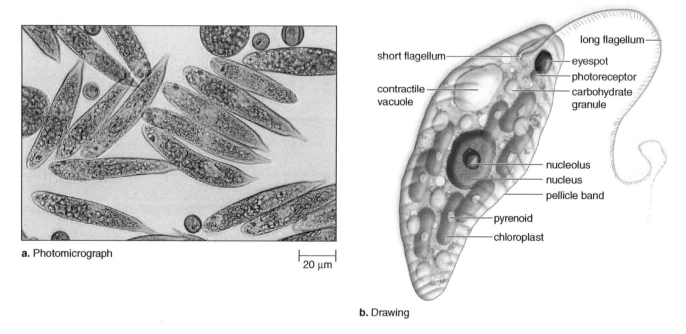

a. Photomicrograph

20 µm

b. Drawing

Pond Water

Examination of pond water will also test your ability to observe objects with the microscope, to utilize depth of field, and to control illumination to heighten contrast.

Laboratory Review 2

1. Make the following conversions:

   a. 1 mm = _____ μm = _____ cm

   b. 15 mm = _____ cm = _____ μm

   c. 50 ml = _____ liter

   d. 5 g = _____ mg

2. Explain the designation "compound light" microscope:

   a. compound _____

   b. light _____

3. What function is performed by the diaphragm of a microscope?

   _____

4. Why is it helpful for a microscope to be parfocal?

   _____

5. Why is locating an object more difficult if you start with the high-power objective than with the low-power objective?

   _____

6. How much larger than normal does an object appear with a low-power objective? _____

   _____

7. A virus is 50 nm in size.

   a. Would you recommend using a stereomicroscope, compound light microscope, or an electron microscope to see it? _____ Why? _____

   _____

   b. How many micrometers is the virus? _____ μm

8. If the diameter of a field is 1.6 mm, and you count forty consecutive cells from one end of the field to the other, how wide is each cell in micrometers? _____ μm

9. What type of microscope, aside from the compound light microscope, might you use to observe the organisms found in pond water? _____

10. Briefly describe the necessary steps for observing a slide at low power under the compound light microscope.

    _____

***Biology* Website**

The companion website for *Biology* provides a wealth of information organized and integrated by chapter. You will find practice tests, animations, videos, and much more that will complement your learning and understanding of general biology.

www.mhhe.com/maderbiology10

McGraw-Hill Access Science Website

An Encyclopedia of Science and Technology Online which provides more information including videos that can enhance the laboratory experience.

www.accessscience.com

3

Chemical Composition of Cells

Learning Outcomes

Introduction

All living things consist of basic units of matter called **atoms.** Molecules form when atoms bond with one another. Inorganic molecules are often associated with nonliving things, and organic molecules are associated with living organisms. In this laboratory, you will be studying the organic molecules of cells: **proteins, carbohydrates** (monosaccharides, disaccharides, polysaccharides), and **lipids** (i.e., fat).

Large organic molecules form during *condensation synthesis* when smaller molecules bond as water is given off. During *hydrolysis,* bonds are broken as water is added. A fat contains one glycerol and three fatty acids. Proteins and some carbohydrates (called polysaccharides) are **polymers** because they are made up of smaller molecules called **monomers.** Proteins contain a large number of amino acids (the monomer) joined together by a peptide bond. A polysaccharide, such as starch, contains a large number of glucose molecules (the monomer) joined together. Various chemicals will be used in this laboratory to test for the presence of cellular organic molecules. If a color change is observed, the test is said to be *positive* because it indicates that the molecule is present. If the color change is not observed, the test is said to be *negative* because it indicates that the molecule is not present.

A control should be included in each experiment for comparison. The **control** will go through all the steps of the experiment, but it will lack the factor being tested. This missing factor allows you to observe the difference between a positive result and a negative result. If the control sample tests positive, you know your test is invalid.

3.1 Proteins

Proteins have numerous functions in cells. Antibodies are proteins that combine with pathogens so that the pathogens are destroyed by the body. Transport proteins combine with and move substances from place to place. Hemoglobin transports oxygen throughout the body. Albumin is another transport protein in our blood. Regulatory proteins control cellular metabolism in some way. For example, the hormone insulin regulates the amount of glucose in blood so that cells have a ready supply. Structural proteins include keratin, found in hair, and myosin, found in muscle. **Enzymes** are proteins that speed chemical reactions. A reaction that could take days or weeks to complete can happen within an instant if the correct enzyme is present. Amylase is an enzyme that speeds the breakdown of starch in the mouth and small intestine.

Proteins are made up of **amino acids** joined together. About 20 different common amino acids are found in cells. All amino acids have an acidic group (—COOH) and an amino group (H_2N—). They differ by the **R group** (remainder group) attached to a carbon atom, as shown in Figure 3.1. The R groups have varying sizes, shapes, and chemical activities.

A chain of two or more amino acids is called a **peptide,** and the bond between the amino acids is called a **peptide bond.** A **polypeptide** is a very long chain of amino acids. A protein can contain one or more polypeptide chains. Insulin contains a single chain, while hemoglobin contains four polypeptides. A protein has a particular shape, which is important to its function. The shape comes about because the R groups of the polypeptide chain(s) can interact with one another in various ways.

Figure 3.1 Peptide bond.
Peptide bond formation between amino acids creates a dipeptide. This dehydration reaction involves the removal of one water molecule. During a hydrolysis reaction, water is added, and the peptide bond is broken. In a polypeptide, many amino acids are held together by multiple peptide bonds.

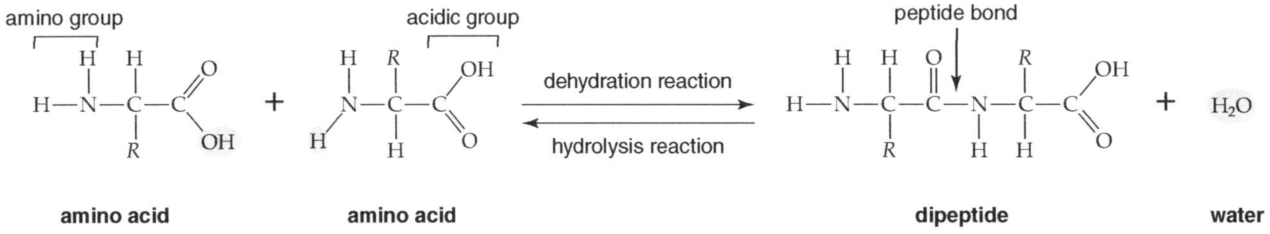

Test for Proteins

Biuret reagent (blue color) contains a strong solution of sodium or potassium hydroxide (NaOH or KOH) and a small amount of dilute copper sulfate ($CuSO_4$) solution. The reagent changes color in the presence of proteins or peptides because the peptide bonds of the protein or peptide chemically combine with the copper ions in biuret reagent (Table 3.1).

Table 3.1 Test for Protein		
	Protein	**Peptides**
Biuret reagent (blue)	Purple	Pinkish-purple

Experimental Procedure: Test for Proteins

With a millimeter ruler and a wax pencil, label and mark four clean test tubes at the 1 cm level. After filling a tube, cover it with Parafilm®, and swirl well to mix. (Do not turn upside down.) The reaction is almost immediate.

> ⚠ **Biuret reagent** Biuret reagent is highly corrosive. Exercise care in using this chemical. If any should spill on your skin, wash the area with mild soap and water. Follow your instructor's directions for its disposal.

*Tube 1
1. Fill to the mark with *distilled water*, and add about five drops of *biuret reagent*.
2. Record the final color in Table 3.2.

Tube 2
1. Fill to the mark with *albumin solution*, and add about five drops of *biuret reagent*.
2. Record the final color in Table 3.2.

Tube 3
1. Fill to the mark with *pepsin solution*, and add about five drops of *biuret reagent*.
2. Record the final color in Table 3.2.

Tube 4
1. Fill to the mark with *starch solution*, and add about five drops of *biuret reagent*.
2. Record the final color in Table 3.2.

Table 3.2 Biuret Test

Tube	Contents	Final Color	Conclusions
1	Distilled water		
2	Albumin		
3	Pepsin		
4	Starch		

Conclusions: Proteins

- Pepsin is an enzyme. Enzymes are composed of what type of organic molecule? _____
- According to your results, is starch a protein? _____
- From your test results, conclude if a protein is present or absent and explain. Enter your conclusions in Table 3.2.
- If your results are not as expected, inform your instructor, who will advise you how to proceed.

_____

- Which of the four tubes is the negative control sample? _____ Why? _____

_____

- Why do experimental procedures include control samples? _____

_____

_____

*To test a sample for protein, use this procedure. Instead of only water, use a liquefied sample. If protein is present, a pinkish-purple color appears.

3.2 Carbohydrates

Carbohydrates include sugars and molecules that are chains of sugars. **Glucose,** which has only one sugar unit, is a monosaccharide; **maltose,** which has two sugar units, is a disaccharide (Fig. 3.2). Glycogen, starch, and cellulose are polysaccharides, made up of chains of glucose units (Fig. 3.3).

Glucose is used by all organisms as an energy source. Energy is released when glucose is broken down to carbon dioxide and water. This energy is used by the organism to do work. Animals store glucose as glycogen and plants store glucose as starch. Plant cell walls are composed of cellulose.

Figure 3.2 Formation of maltose, a disaccharide.
During a dehydration reaction, a bond forms between the two glucose molecules, the components of water are removed, and maltose results. During a hydrolysis reaction, the components of water are added, and the bond is broken.

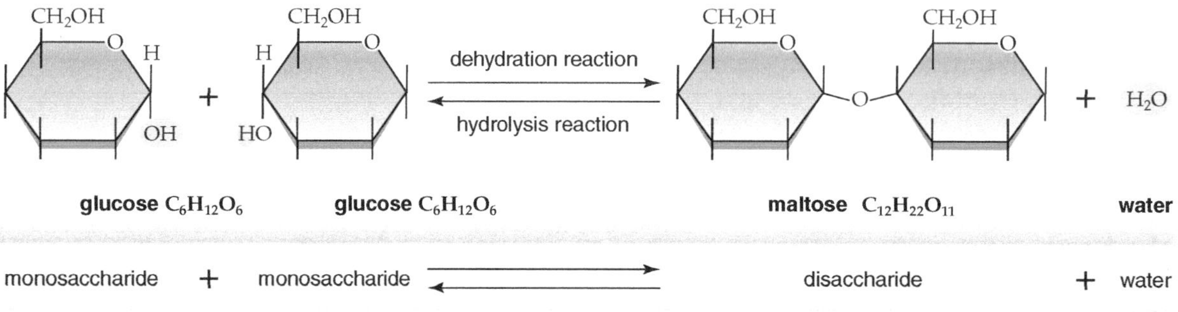

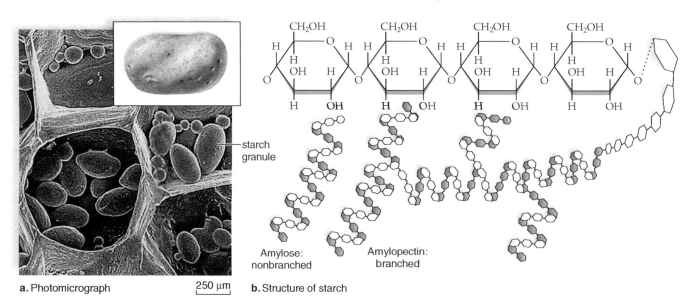

glucose $C_6H_{12}O_6$ glucose $C_6H_{12}O_6$ maltose $C_{12}H_{22}O_{11}$ water

monosaccharide + monosaccharide   disaccharide + water

Figure 3.3 Starch.
Starch is a polysaccharide composed of many glucose units. **a.** Photomicrograph of starch granules in plant cells. **b.** Structure of starch. Starch consists of amylose that is nonbranched and amylopectin that is branched.

starch granule

Amylose: nonbranched   Amylopectin: branched

a. Photomicrograph   250 μm   **b.** Structure of starch

Test for Starch

In the presence of starch, iodine solution (yellowish-brown) reacts chemically with starch to form a blue-black color.

Experimental Procedure: Test for Starch

With a wax pencil, label and mark five clean test tubes at the 1 cm level.

*Tube 1
1. Fill to the 1 cm mark with *water,* and add five drops of *iodine solution.*
2. Note the final color change, and record your results in Table 3.3.

Tube 2
1. It is very important to shake the *starch suspension* well before taking your sample. After shaking, fill this tube to the 1 cm mark with the 1% *starch suspension.* Add five drops of *iodine solution.*
2. Note the final color change, and record your results in Table 3.3.

Tube 3
1. Add a few drops of *onion juice* to the test tube. (Obtain the juice by adding water and crushing a small piece of onion with a mortar and pestle. Clean mortar and pestle after using.) Add five drops of *iodine solution.*
2. Note the final color change, and record your results in Table 3.3.

Tube 4
1. Add a few drops of *potato juice* to the test tube. (Obtain the juice by adding water and crushing a small piece of potato with a mortar and pestle. Clean mortar and pestle after using.) Add five drops of *iodine solution.*
2. Note the final color change, and record your results in Table 3.3.

Tube 5
1. Fill to the 1 cm mark with *glucose solution,* and add five drops of *iodine solution.*
2. Note the final color change, and record your results in Table 3.3.

Table 3.3 Iodine (IKI) Tests for Starch

Tube	Contents	Color	Conclusions
1	Water		
2	Starch suspension		
3	Onion juice		
4	Potato juice		
5	Glucose solution		

Conclusions: Starch

- Does the potato or the onion store glucose as starch? _____ How do you know? _____
  _____

- From your test results, draw conclusions about what organic compound is present in each tube. Write these conclusions in Table 3.3.
- If your results are not as expected, offer an explanation. Then inform your instructor, who will advise you how to proceed.

*To test a sample for starch, use this procedure. Instead of only water, use a liquefied sample. If starch is present, a blue-black color appears.

Experimental Procedure: Microscopic Study

Potato

1. With a sharp razor blade, slice a very thin piece of potato. Place it on a microscope slide, add a drop of *water* and a coverslip, and observe under low power with your compound light microscope. Compare your slide with the photomicrograph of starch granules (see Fig. 3.3*a*). Find the cell wall (large, geometric compartments) and the starch grains (numerous clear, oval-shaped objects).
2. Without removing the coverslip, place two drops of *iodine solution* onto the microscope slide so that the iodine touches the coverslip. Draw the iodine under the coverslip by placing a small piece of paper towel in contact with the water on the **opposite** side of the coverslip.
3. Microscopically examine the potato again on the side closest to where the iodine solution was applied.

    What is the color of the small, oval bodies? _____

    What is the chemical composition of these oval bodies? _____

Onion

1. Peel a single layer of onion from the bulb. On the inside surface, you will find a thin, transparent layer of onion skin. Peel off a small section of this layer for use on your slide.
2. Add a large drop of *iodine solution*.
3. Does onion contain starch? _____
4. Are these results consistent with those you recorded for onions in Table 3.3? _____

Test for Sugars

⚠️ **Benedict's reagent** Benedict's reagent is highly corrosive. Exercise care in using this chemical. If any should spill on your skin, wash the area with mild soap and water. Follow your instructor's directions for disposal of this chemical.

Monosaccharides and some disaccharides will react with **Benedict's reagent** after being heated in a boiling water bath. In this reaction, copper ion (Cu^{2+}) in the Benedict's reagent reacts with part of the sugar molecule and is reduced, causing a distinctive color change. The color change can range from green to red, and increasing concentrations of sugar will give a continuum of colored products (Table 3.4).

Table 3.4 Benedict's Reagent (Some Typical Reactions)

Chemical	Chemical Category	Benedict's Reagent (After Heating)
Water	Inorganic	Blue (no change)
Glucose	Monosaccharide (carbohydrate)	Varies with concentration: very low—green low—yellow moderate—yellow-orange high—orange very high—orange-red
Maltose	Disaccharide (carbohydrate)	Varies with concentration—see "Glucose"
Starch	Polysaccharide (carbohydrate)	Blue (no change)

Experimental Procedure: Test for Sugars

(This procedure runs for one hour. Prior setup can maximize time efficiency.)
With a wax pencil, label and mark five clean test tubes at the 1 cm level. Save your tubes for comparison with Section 3.4.

*Tube 1
1. Fill to the 1 cm mark with *water,* then add about five drops of *Benedict's reagent.*
2. Heat in a boiling water bath for 5 to 10 minutes, note any color change, and record in Table 3.5.

Tube 2
1. Fill to the 1 cm mark with *glucose solution,* then add about five drops of *Benedict's reagent.*
2. Heat in a boiling water bath for 5 to 10 minutes, note any color change, and record in Table 3.5.

Tube 3
1. Fill to the 1 cm mark with *starch suspension,* then add about five drops of *Benedict's reagent.*
2. Heat in a boiling water bath for 5 to 10 minutes, note any color change, and record in Table 3.5.

Tube 4
1. Place a few drops of *onion juice* in the test tube. (Obtain the juice by adding water and crushing a small piece of onion with a mortar and pestle. Clean mortar and pestle after using.)
2. Fill to the 1 cm mark with *water,* then add about five drops of *Benedict's reagent.*
3. Heat in a boiling water bath for 5 to 10 minutes, note any color change, and record in Table 3.5.

Tube 5
1. Place a few drops of *potato juice* in the test tube. (Obtain the juice by adding water and crushing a small piece of potato with a mortar and pestle.)
2. Fill to the 1 cm mark with *water,* then add about five drops of *Benedict's reagent.*
3. Heat in a boiling water bath for 5 to 10 minutes, note any color change, and record in Table 3.5.

Table 3.5 Benedict's Reagent Test

Tube	Contents	Color (After Heating)	Conclusions
1	Water		
2	Glucose solution		
3	Starch suspension		
4	Onion juice		
5	Potato juice		

Conclusions: Sugars

- From your test results, conclude what kind of chemical is present. Enter your conclusions in Table 3.5.

- Which tubes served as a control? _____

*To test a sample for sugars, use this procedure. Instead of only water, use a liquefied sample. If sugar is present, a green to orange-red color appears.

- Compare Table 3.3 with Table 3.5. Sugars are an immediate energy source in cells. In plant cells, glucose (a primary energy molecule) is often stored in the form of starch. Is glucose stored **as starch** in the potato? _____ Is glucose stored as starch in the onion? _____ Does this explain your results in Table 3.5? _____ Why? _____

Starch Composition

Pancreatic amylase is an enzyme that speeds the breakdown of starch to maltose by hydrolysis:

$$\text{starch} + \text{water} \xrightarrow{\text{pancreatic amylase}} \text{maltose}$$

Experimental Procedure: Starch Composition

(This procedure requires a 30 minute reaction time. Prior setup can maximize time efficiency.)
With a wax pencil, label and mark two clean test tubes at the 2 cm, 4 cm, and 6 cm levels. Save your tubes for comparison with Section 3.4.

Tube 1
1. Fill to the 2 cm mark with *water* and to the 4 cm mark with 1% *pancreatic amylase*.
2. Shake and then wait for 30 minutes.
3. Add *Benedict's reagent* to the 6 cm level and heat in a boiling water bath.
4. Note any color change, and record your results in Table 3.6.

Tube 2
1. Fill to the 2 cm mark with *starch* and to the 4 cm mark with *pancreatic amylase*.
2. Shake and then wait for 30 minutes.
3. Add *Benedict's reagent* and heat as before.
4. Note any color change, and record your results in Table 3.6.

Save your positive test results for use in Section 3.4.

Table 3.6	Starch Composition		
Tube	**Contents**	**Color Change**	**Conclusions**
1	Water Pancreatic amylase		
2	Starch Pancreatic amylase		

Conclusions: Starch Composition

- From your test results, you may conclude that starch is composed of what kind of chemical?

_____

- How do you know? _____

Enter your conclusions in Table 3.6.

3.3 Lipids

Lipids are compounds that are insoluble in water and soluble in solvents, such as alcohol and ether. Lipids include fats, oils, phospholipids, steroids, and cholesterol. Typically, fats and oils are composed of three molecules of fatty acids bonded to one molecule of glycerol (Fig. 3.4). Phospholipids have the same structure as fats, except in place of the third fatty acid there is a phosphate group (a grouping that contains phosphate). Steroids are derived from cholesterol and, like this molecule, have skeletons of four fused rings of carbon atoms, but they differ by functional groups (attached side chains). Fat, as we know, is long-term stored energy in the human body. Phospholipids are found in the plasma membrane of cells. In recent years, cholesterol, a molecule transported in the blood, has been implicated in causing cardiovascular disease. Regardless, steroids are very important compounds in the body; for example, the sex hormones are steroids.

Test for Fat

Fats do not evaporate from brown paper; instead, they leave an oily spot.

Experimental Procedure: Test for Fat

*1. Place a small drop of *water* on a square of brown paper. Describe the immediate effect. _____

_____

2. Place a small drop of *vegetable oil* on a square of brown paper. Describe the immediate effect.

_____

3. Wait at least 15 minutes for the paper to dry. Evaluate which substance penetrates the paper and which is subject to evaporation. Record your observations and conclusions in Table 3.7. Save the paper for comparison with Section 3.4.

Table 3.7 Test for Fat		
Sample	**Observations**	**Conclusions**
Water spot		
Oil spot		

Figure 3.4 Formation of a fat.
A fat molecule forms when glycerol joins with three fatty acids as three water molecules are removed during a dehydration reaction. During a hydrolysis reaction, water is added, and the bonds are broken.

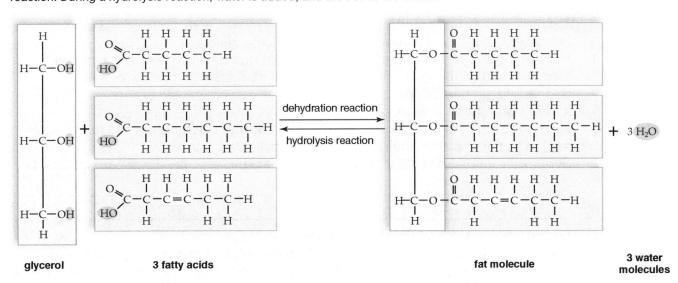

glycerol   3 fatty acids   fat molecule   3 water molecules

*To test an unknown for fat, use this procedure. Do not liquefy the sample; place it as is on a piece of brown paper over the sink, in order to facilitate cleanup. If lipids are present, an oily spot appears.

Emulsification of Lipids

Some molecules are **polar,** meaning that they have charged groups or atoms, and some are **nonpolar,** meaning that they have no charged groups or atoms. A water molecule is polar, and therefore, water is a good solvent for other polar molecules. When the charged ends of water molecules interact with the charged groups of polar molecules, these polar molecules disperse in water.

Water is not a good solvent for nonpolar molecules, such as fats. A fat has no polar groups to interact with water molecules. An **emulsifier,** however, can cause a fat to disperse in water. An emulsifier contains molecules with both polar and nonpolar ends. When the nonpolar ends interact with the fat and the polar ends interact with the water molecules, the fat disperses in water, and an *emulsion* results (Fig. 3.5).

Bile salts (emulsifiers found in bile produced by the liver) are used in the digestive tract. Commercially produced emulsifiers include detergents and the wetting agent Tween®.

Figure 3.5 Emulsification.
An emulsifier contains molecules with both a polar and a nonpolar end. The nonpolar ends are attracted to the nonpolar fat, and the polar ends are attracted to the water. This causes droplets of fat molecules to disperse.

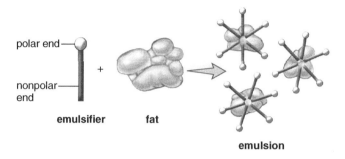

Experimental Procedure: Emulsification of Lipids

With a wax pencil, label two clean test tubes 1 and 2. Mark tube 1 at the 3 cm and 4 cm levels. Mark tube 2 at the 2 cm, 3 cm, and 4 cm levels.

Tube 1
1. Fill to the 3 cm mark with *water* and to the 4 cm mark with *vegetable oil.* Shake.
2. Observe for the initial dispersal of oil, followed by rapid separation into two layers. Is vegetable oil soluble in water? _____
3. Let the tube settle for 5 minutes. Label a microscope slide as 1.
4. Use a dropper to remove a sample of the solution that is just below the layer of oil. Place the drop on the slide, add a coverslip, and examine with the low power of your compound light microscope.
5. Record your observations in Table 3.8.

Tube 2
1. Fill to the 2 cm mark with *water,* to the 3 cm mark with *vegetable oil,* and to the 4 cm mark with the available emulsifier (*Tween®* or *bile salts*). Shake.
2. Describe how the distribution of oil in tube 2 compares with the distribution in tube 1.

_____

_____

3. Let the tube settle for 5 minutes. Label a microscope slide as 2.
4. Use a different dropper to remove a sample of the solution that is just below the layer of oil. Place the drop on the slide, add a coverslip, and examine with the low power of your compound light microscope.
5. Record your observations in Table 3.8.

Table 3.8 Emulsification

Tube	Contents	Observations	Conclusions
1	Oil Water		
2	Oil Water Emulsifier		

Conclusions : Fat

- From your observations, conclude why the contents of tube 1 and tube 2 appear as they do under the microscope. Record your conclusions in Table 3.8.
- Explain the correlation between your macroscopic observations (how the tubes look to your unaided eye) and your microscopic observations. _____

_____

Adipose Tissue

Adipose tissue stores droplets of fat. Adipose tissue is found beneath the skin, where it helps insulate and keep the body warm. It also forms a protective cushion around various internal organs.

Observation: Adipose Tissue

1. Obtain a slide of adipose tissue, and view it under the microscope at high power. Refer to Figure 3.6 for help in identifying the structures.
2. Notice how the fat droplets push the cytoplasm to the edges of the cells.

Figure 3.6 Adipose tissue.
The cells are so full of fat that the nucleus is pushed to one side.

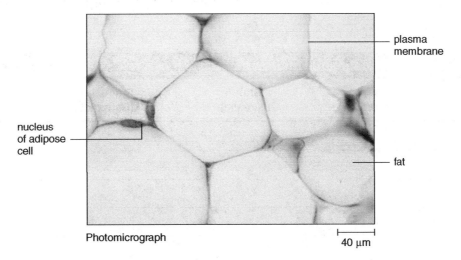

Photomicrograph

40 μm

3.4 Testing the Chemical Composition of Everyday Materials and an Unknown

Everyday materials, such as foods, are derived from cells and, therefore, are composed of organic compounds—proteins, carbohydrates, and lipids. In the following Experimental Procedure, you will determine whether these organic substances are present in various everyday materials by using the tests you learned in previous sections of this laboratory.

Experimental Procedure: Chemical Composition

Read through these instructions before doing any testing.

1. Obtain a small sample of the substance you will be testing. For all tests (except the one for lipid), you will need a liquefied sample as provided by your instructor.
2. Your instructor may have you work in groups, in which case you may need to do only one test for each substance you will be testing.
3. Obtain a test tube. To identify the substance you will be testing, use a wax pencil to write on the tube; label either by letter or name of substance. Work with only one substance at a time, and complete the first column of Table 3.9 for this substance only.
4. With a wax pencil, label and mark the test tube at the 1 cm level. Fill to the 1 cm mark with the liquefied substance.
5. To test, you will need to go the appropriate page in your lab manual:

    To test for protein, go to page 29 and follow the instructions for tube 1, using your liquefied sample instead of only water. After observing your results, see step 6 for recording results.

    To test for starch, go to page 31 and follow the instructions for tube 1, using your liquefied sample instead of only water. After observing your results, see step 6 for recording results.

    To test for sugar, go to page 33 and follow the instructions for tube 1, using your liquefied sample instead of only water. After observing your results, see step 6 for recording results.

    To test for lipid, go to page 35 and follow the instructions for step 1. Do not liquefy the sample, place it as is on a piece of brown paper over the sink. Catching any spillage over the sink will facilitate cleanup. After observing your results, see step 6 for recording results.

6. Record your results in Table 3.9.

Table 3.9 Everyday Materials and Unknowns				
Substance	Protein (Biuret)	Starch (Iodine)	Sugar (Benedict's)	Lipid (Brown Paper)
1.				
2.				
3.				
Unknown A				
Unknown B				

Instead of recording a color change, use a (+) to indicate a positive result and (−) to indicate a negative result. In other words, a (+) would mean that the organic compound is present, and a (−) would mean that the organic compound is not present.

If you are a member of a team, also record the results of your team members for this substance.

7. Go to Conclusions: Everyday Materials to complete your study of this substance.

Conclusions : Everyday Materials

- Substance 1 _____

From your results, what organic compounds are present in this substance? _____

_____

Is this what you would have expected for this substance? _____ Explain. _____

_____

If you have difficulty giving an explanation, think about how this substance is utilized by the plant or animal that produced it or how it is utilized by humans. Discuss your thoughts with your lab partners or your instructor before giving an explanation.

- Substance 2 _____

From your results, what organic compounds are present in this substance? _____

_____

Is this what you would have expected for this substance? _____Explain. _____

_____

- Substance 3 _____

From your results, what organic compounds are present in this substance? _____

_____

Is this what you would have expected for this substance? _____ Explain. _____

_____

Overall Conclusion

Does your study lead you to conclude that many everyday substances contain organic compounds? _____Offer an explanation.

Laboratory Review 3

1. What organic molecules studied today are present in cells? _____

_____

2. You have been assigned the task of constructing a protein. What type of building block would you use?

_____

3. A digestive enzyme such as pancreatic amylase breaks down starch to what disaccharide studied in this

   laboratory? _____

4. Why is it necessary to shake an oil and vinegar salad dressing before adding it to a salad? _____

_____

5. How would you test an unknown solution for each of the following:

   a. Sugars _____

   b. Fat _____

   c. Starch _____

   d. Protein _____

6. Assume that you have tested an unknown sample with both biuret solution and Benedict's reagent and

   that both tests result in a blue color. What have you learned? _____

_____

7. What purpose is served when a test is done using water instead of a sample substance? _____

_____

8. A test tube contains starch, pancreatic amylase, and water. The biuret test is negative. After 30 minutes,

   the Benedict's test is positive. What substance is present? _____

9. A test tube contains albumin and pepsin. The test for protein is positive. Explain.

_____

Although pepsin is an enzyme that breaks down protein, a test for peptides is negative. Explain.

_____

LABORATORY

4
Cell Structure and Function

Learning Outcomes

4.1 Prokaryotic Versus Eukaryotic Cells
- Distinguish between prokaryotic and eukaryotic cells by description and examples.   42

4.2 Animal Cell and Plant Cell Structure
- Label an animal cell diagram, and state a function for the structures labeled.   43–44
- Label a plant cell diagram, and state a function for the structures labeled.   45
- Use microscopic techniques to observe plant cell structure.   46

4.3 Diffusion
- Define and describe the process of diffusion.   47
- Predict and observe which substances will or will not diffuse across a plasma membrane.   47–49

4.4 Osmosis: Diffusion of Water Across Plasma Membrane
- Explain an osmosis experiment based on a knowledge of diffusion principles.   49–50
- Define isotonic, hypertonic, and hypotonic solutions, and give examples in terms of NaCl concentrations.   51
- Predict the effect of different tonicities on animal (e.g., red blood) cells and on plant (e.g., *Elodea*) cells.   51–53

4.5 pH and Cells
- Predict the change in pH before and after the addition of an acid to nonbuffered and buffered solutions.   54
- Suggest a method by which it is possible to test the effectiveness of antacid medications.   54–55

Introduction

The molecules we studied in the last laboratory are not alive—the basic units of life are cells. The **cell theory** states that all living things are composed of cells and that cells come only from other cells. While we are accustomed to considering the heart, the liver, or the intestines as enabling the human body to function, it is actually cells that do the work of these organs.

Figure 4.1 is a human cheek epithelial cell as viewed by an ordinary compound light microscope available in general biology laboratories. It shows that the content of a cell, called the **cytoplasm,** is bounded by a **plasma membrane.** The plasma membrane regulates the movement of molecules into and out of the cytoplasm. In this lab, we will study how the passage of water into a cell depends on the difference in concentration of solutes (particles) between the cytoplasm and the surrounding medium or solution. The well-being of cells also depends upon the pH of the solution surrounding them. We will see how a buffer can maintain the pH within a narrow range and how buffers within cells can protect them against damaging pH changes.

Because a photomicrograph shows only a minimal amount of detail, it is necessary to turn to the electron microscope to study the contents of a cell in greater depth. The models of plant and animal cells available in the laboratory today are based on electron micrographs.

Figure 4.1   Photomicrograph of an epithelial cell.
(Magnification 250x)

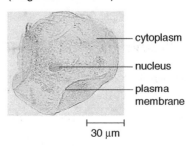
30 µm

4.1 Prokaryotic Versus Eukaryotic Cells

All living cells are classified as either prokaryotic or eukaryotic. One of the basic differences between the two types is that prokaryotic cells do not contain nuclei (*pro* means "before"; *karyote* means "nucleus"), while eukaryotic cells do contain nuclei (*eu* means "true"; *karyote* means "nucleus"). Only bacteria (including cyanobacteria) and archaea are prokaryotes; all other organisms are eukaryotes.

Prokaryotes also don't have the organelles found in eukaryotic cells (Fig. 4.2). **Organelles** are small, membranous bodies, each with a specific structure and function. Prokaryotes do have **cytoplasm,** the material bounded by a plasma membrane and cell wall. The cytoplasm contains ribosomes, small granules that coordinate the synthesis of proteins; thylakoids (only in cyanobacteria) that participate in photosynthesis; and innumerable enzymes. Prokaryotes also have a nucleoid, a region in the bacterial cell interior in which the DNA is physically organized but not enclosed by a membrane.

Figure 4.2 Prokaryotic cell.
Prokaryotic cells lack membrane-bounded organelles, as well as a nucleus. Their DNA is in a nucleoid region.

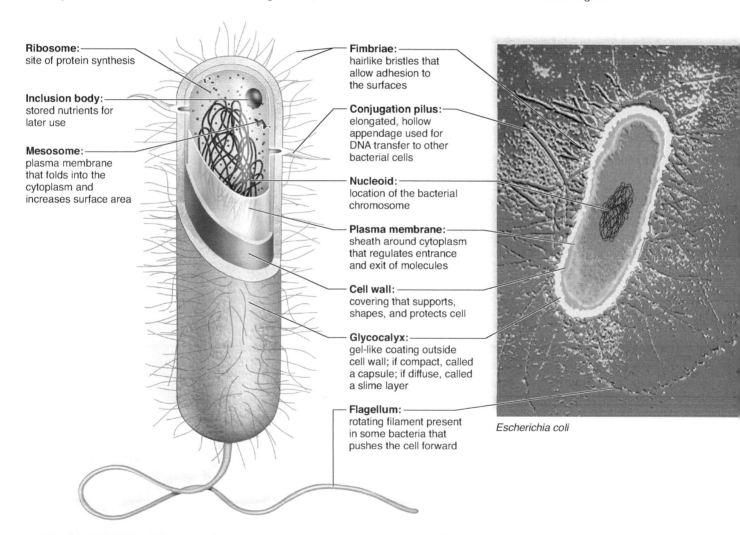

Ribosome: site of protein synthesis

Inclusion body: stored nutrients for later use

Mesosome: plasma membrane that folds into the cytoplasm and increases surface area

Fimbriae: hairlike bristles that allow adhesion to the surfaces

Conjugation pilus: elongated, hollow appendage used for DNA transfer to other bacterial cells

Nucleoid: location of the bacterial chromosome

Plasma membrane: sheath around cytoplasm that regulates entrance and exit of molecules

Cell wall: covering that supports, shapes, and protects cell

Glycocalyx: gel-like coating outside cell wall; if compact, called a capsule; if diffuse, called a slime layer

Flagellum: rotating filament present in some bacteria that pushes the cell forward

Escherichia coli

Observation: Prokaryotic/Eukaryotic Cells

Two microscope slides on display will show you the main difference between prokaryotic and eukaryotic cells.

1. Examine a prepared slide of a prokaryote. There are no nuclei in these cells.

2. Examine a prepared slide of cuboidal cells from a human kidney (see page 420). You can make out a nucleus.

4.2 Animal Cell and Plant Cell Structure

Table 4.1 lists the structures found in animal and plant cells. The **nucleus** in a eukaryotic cell is bounded by a **nuclear envelope** and contains **nucleoplasm.** The *cytoplasm,* found between the plasma membrane and the nucleus, consists of a background fluid and the organelles. Many **organelles** are membranous, such as the nucleolus, endoplasmic reticulum, Golgi apparatus, vacuoles and vesicles, lysosomes, peroxisome, mitochondrion, and chloroplast.

Table 4.1 Eukaryotic Structures in Animal Cells and Plant Cells

Name	Composition	Function
Cell wall*	Contains cellulose fibrils	Provides support and protection
Plasma membrane	Phospholipid bilayer with embedded proteins	Outer cell surface that regulates entrance and exit of molecules
Nucleus	Enclosed by nuclear envelope; contains chromatin (threads of DNA and protein)	Storage of genetic information; synthesis of DNA and RNA
Nucleolus	Concentrated area of chromatin	Produces subunits of ribosomes
Ribosome	Protein and RNA in two subunits	Carries out protein synthesis
Endoplasmic reticulum (ER)	Membranous, flattened channels and tubular canals; rough ER and smooth ER	Synthesis and/or modification of proteins and other substances; transport by vesicle formation
Rough ER	Studded with ribosomes	Protein synthesis
Smooth ER	Lacks ribosomes	Synthesis of lipid molecules
Golgi apparatus	Stack of membranous saccules	Processes, packages, and distributes proteins and lipids
Vesicle	Membrane-bounded sac	Stores and transports substances
Lysosome	Vesicle containing hydrolytic enzymes	Digests macromolecules and cell parts
Peroxisome	Vesicle containing specific enzymes	Breaks down fatty acids and converts resulting hydrogen peroxide to water; various other functions
Mitochondrion	Membranous cristae bounded by double membrane	Carries out cellular respiration, producing ATP molecules
Chloroplast*	Membranous thylakoids bounded by double membrane	Carries out photosynthesis, producing sugars
Cytoskeleton	Microtubules, intermediate filaments, actin filaments	Maintains cell shape and assists movement of cell parts
Cilia and flagella	9 + 2 pattern of microtubules	Movement of cell
Centrioles**	9 + 0 pattern of microtubules	Unknown function

*Plant cells only
**Animal cells only

Study Table 4.1 to determine structures that are unique to plant cells and unique to animal cells, and write them below the examples given.

	Plant Cells	**Animal Cells**
Unique structures:	1. Large central vacuole	1. Small vacuoles
	2. _____	2. _____
	3. _____	

Animal Cell Structure

With the help of Table 4.1, give a function for each of these structures, and label Figure 4.3.

Structure   Function

Plasma membrane _____

Nucleus _____

Nucleolus _____

Ribosome _____

Endoplasmic reticulum _____

     Rough ER _____

     Smooth ER _____

Golgi apparatus _____

Vesicles _____

Lysosome _____

Mitochondrion _____

Centrioles in centrosome _____

Cytoskeleton _____

Figure 4.3   Animal cell structure.

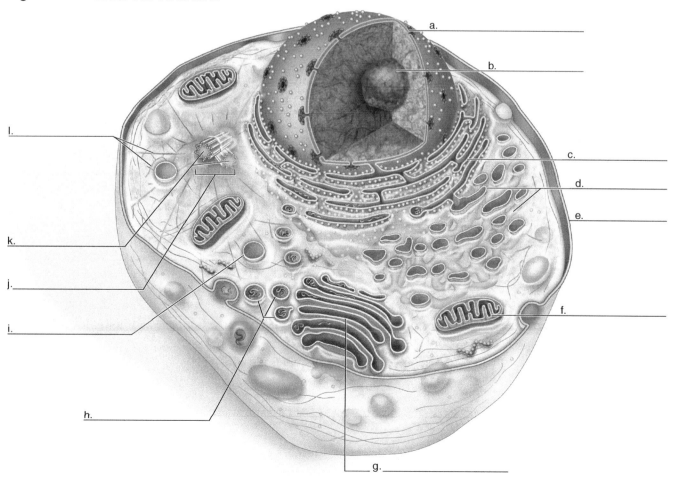

Plant Cell Structure

With the help of Table 4.1, give a function for these structures unique to plant cells, and label Figure 4.4.

Structure	Function
Cell wall	_____
Central vacuole, large	_____
Chloroplasts	_____

Figure 4.4   Plant cell structure.

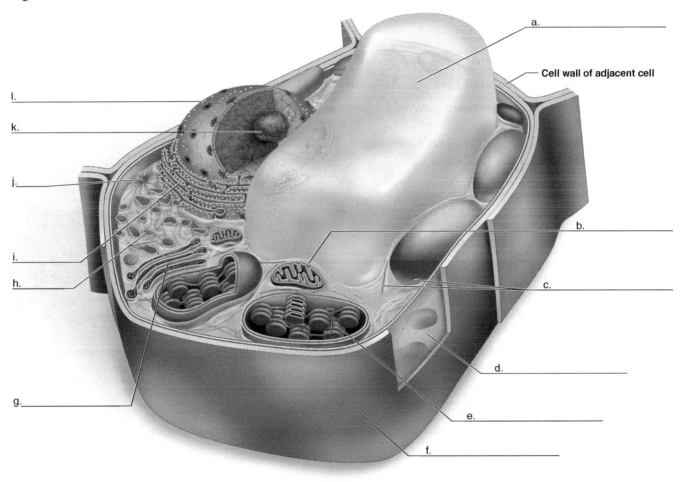

Cell wall of adjacent cell

Observation: Plant Cell Structure

1. Prepare a wet mount of a small piece of young *Elodea* leaf in fresh water. *Elodea* is a multi-cellular, eukaryotic plant found in freshwater ponds and lakes.
2. Have the drop of *water* ready on your slide so that the leaf does not dry out, even for a few seconds. Take care that the leaf is mounted with its top side up.
3. Examine the slide using low power, focusing sharply on the leaf surface.
4. Select a cell with numerous chloroplasts for further study, and switch to high power.
5. Carefully focus on the side and end walls of the cell. The chloroplasts appear to be only along the sides of the cell because the large, fluid-filled, membrane-bounded central vacuole pushes the cytoplasm against the cell walls (Fig. 4.5*a*). Then focus on the surface and notice an even distribution of chloroplasts (Fig. 4.5*b*).
6. Can you locate the cell nucleus? _____ It may be hidden by the chloroplasts, but when visible, it appears as a faint, grey lump on one side of the cell.
7. Can you detect movement of chloroplasts in this cell or any other cell? _____ The chloroplasts are not moving under their own power but are being carried by a streaming of the nearly invisible cytoplasm.
8. Save your slide for use later in this laboratory.

Figure 4.5   *Elodea* cell structure.

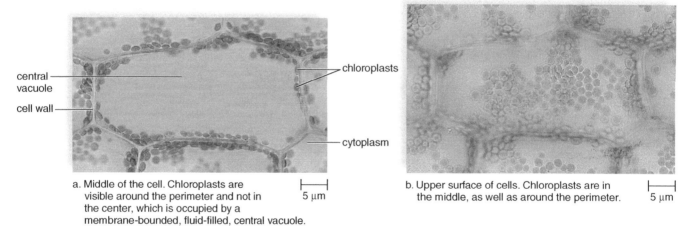

a. Middle of the cell. Chloroplasts are visible around the perimeter and not in the center, which is occupied by a membrane-bounded, fluid-filled, central vacuole.

⊢——⊣ 5 μm

b. Upper surface of cells. Chloroplasts are in the middle, as well as around the perimeter.

⊢——⊣ 5 μm

4.3 Diffusion

Diffusion is the movement of molecules from a higher to a lower concentration until equilibrium is achieved and the molecules are distributed equally (Fig. 4.6). At this point, molecules may still be moving back and forth, but there is no net movement in any one direction.

Figure 4.6 Process of diffusion.
Diffusion is apparent when dye molecules have equally dispersed.

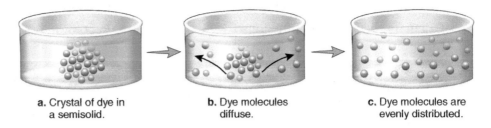

a. Crystal of dye in a semisolid.

b. Dye molecules diffuse.

c. Dye molecules are evenly distributed.

Diffusion is a general phenomenon in the environment. The speed of diffusion is dependent on such factors as the temperature, the size of the molecule, and the type of medium.

Experimental Procedure: Diffusion

Solute Diffusion Through a Semisolid

1. Observe a petri dish containing 1.5% gelatin (or agar) to which potassium permanganate ($KMnO_4$) was added in the center depression at the beginning of the lab.

> ⚠️ **Potassium permanganate $KMnO_4$** $KMnO_4$ is highly poisonous and is a strong oxidizer. Avoid contact with skin and eyes and wash combustible materials. If spillage occurs, wash all surfaces thoroughly. $KMnO_4$ will also stain clothing.

2. Obtain *time zero* from your instructor, and record *time zero* and the *final time* (now) in Table 4.2. Calculate the length of time in hours and minutes. Convert the time to hours: _____ hr.

3. Using a ruler placed over the petri dish, measure (in mm) the movement of color from the center of the depression outward in one direction: _____ mm.

4. Calculate the speed of diffusion: _____ mm/hr.

5. Record all data in Table 4.2.

Solute Diffusion Through a Liquid

1. Add enough water to cover the bottom of a glass petri dish.

2. Place the petri dish over a thin, flat ruler.

3. With tweezers, add a crystal of potassium permanganate ($KMnO_4$) directly over a millimeter measurement line. Note the *time zero* in Table 4.2.

4. After 10 minutes, note the distance the color has moved. Record the *final time, length of time,* and *distance moved* in Table 4.2.

5. Multiply the length of time and the distance moved by 6 to calculate the *speed of diffusion:* _____ mm/hr. Record in Table 4.2.

Diffusion Through Air

1. Measure the distance from a spot designated by your instructor to your laboratory work area today. Record this distance in the fifth column of Table 4.2.
2. Record *time zero* in Table 4.2 when a perfume or similar substance is released into the air.
3. Note the time when you can smell the perfume. Record this as the *final time* in Table 4.2. Calculate the *length of time* since the perfume was released, and record it in Table 4.2.
4. Calculate the speed of diffusion: _____ mm/hr. Record in Table 4.2.

Table 4.2 Speed of Diffusion					
Medium	Time Zero	Final Time	Length of Time (hr)	Distance Moved (mm)	Speed of Diffusion (mm/hr)
Semisolid					
Liquid					
Air					

Conclusions: Solute Diffusion

- In which experiment was diffusion the fastest? _____
- What accounts for the difference in speed? _____

Solute Diffusion Across the Plasma Membrane

Some molecules can diffuse across a plasma membrane, and some cannot. In general, small, noncharged molecules can cross a membrane by simple diffusion, but large molecules cannot diffuse across a membrane. The dialysis tube membrane in the experimental procedure simulates a plasma membrane.

Experimental Procedure: Solute Diffusion Across Plasma Membrane

At the start of the experiment,

1. Cut a piece of dialysis tubing approximately 40 cm (approximately 16 in) long. Soak the tubing in water until it is soft and pliable.
2. Close one end of the dialysis tubing with two knots.
3. Fill the bag halfway with *glucose solution*.
4. Add 4 full droppers of *starch solution* to the bag.
5. Hold the open end while you mix the contents of the dialysis bag. Rinse off the outside of the bag with *distilled water*.
6. Fill a beaker 2/3 full with *distilled water*.
7. Add droppers of *iodine solution* (IKI) to the water in the beaker until an amber (tealike) color is apparent.
8. Record the color of the solution in the beaker in Table 4.3.

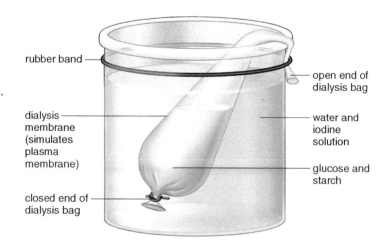

Figure 4.7 Placement of dialysis bag in water containing iodine.

rubber band

open end of dialysis bag

dialysis membrane (simulates plasma membrane)

water and iodine solution

glucose and starch

closed end of dialysis bag

9. Place the bag in the beaker with the open end hanging over the edge. Secure the open end of the bag to the beaker with a rubber band as shown (Fig. 4.7). Make sure the contents do not spill into the beaker.

After about 5 minutes, at the end of the experiment,

10. You will note a color change. Record the color of the bag contents in Table 4.3.
11. Mark off a test tube at 1 cm and 3 cm.
12. Draw solution from near the bag and at the bottom of the beaker for testing with Benedict's reagent. Fill the test tube to the first mark with this solution. Add *Benedict's reagent* to the 3 cm mark. Heat in a boiling water bath for 5 to 10 minutes, observe any color change, and record your results as positive or negative in Table 4.3. (Optional use of glucose test strip: Dip glucose test strip into beaker. Compare stick with chart provided by instructor.)
13. Remove the dialysis bag from the beaker. Dispose of it and the used Benedict's reagent solution in the manner directed by your instructor.

> ⚠️ **Benedict's reagent** Benedict's reagent is highly corrosive. Exercise care in using this chemical. If any should spill on your skin, wash the area with mild soap and water. Follow your instructor's directions for disposal of this chemical.

Table 4.3 Solute Diffusion Across Plasma Membrane

| | At Start of Experiment | | At End of Experiment | | |
	Contents	Color	Color	Benedict's Test (+) or (−)	Conclusion
Bag	Glucose Starch	—		—	
Beaker	Water Iodine		—		

Conclusions: Solute Diffusion Across the Plasma Membrane

- Based on the color change noted in the bag, conclude what solute diffused across the dialysis membrane from the beaker to the bag, and record your conclusion in Table 4.3.
- From the results of the Benedict's test on the beaker contents, conclude what solute diffused across the dialysis membrane from the bag to the beaker, and record your conclusion in Table 4.3.
- Which solute did not diffuse across the dialysis membrane from the bag to the beaker?

_____ Explain. _____

4.4 Osmosis: Diffusion of Water Across Plasma Membrane

Osmosis is the diffusion of water across the plasma membrane of a cell. Just like any other molecule, water follows its concentration gradient and moves from the area of higher concentration to the area of lower concentration.

Experimental Procedure: Osmosis

To demonstrate osmosis, a thistle tube is covered with a membrane at its lower opening and partially filled with 50% corn syrup (starch solution) or a similar substance. The whole apparatus is placed in a beaker containing distilled water (Fig. 4.8). The water concentration in the beaker is 100%. Water molecules can move freely between the thistle tube and the beaker.

1. Note the level of liquid in the thistle tube, and measure how far it travels in 10 minutes: _____ mm.

2. Calculate the speed of osmosis under these conditions: _____ mm/hr.

Conclusions: Osmosis

- In which direction was there a net movement of water? _____
  Explain what is meant by "net movement" after examining the arrows in Figure 4.8b.

  _____

- If the starch molecules in corn syrup moved from the thistle tube to the beaker, would there have been a net movement of water into the thistle tube? _____ Why wouldn't large starch molecules be able to move across the membrane from the thistle tube to the beaker?

  _____

- Explain why the water level in the thistle tube rose: In terms of solvent concentration, water moved from the area of _____ water concentration to the area of _____ water concentration across a differentially permeable membrane.

Figure 4.8 Osmosis demonstration.

a. A thistle tube, covered at the broad end by a differentially permeable membrane, contains a corn syrup solution. The beaker contains distilled water. **b.** The solute is unable to pass through the membrane (red), but the water (arrows) passes through in both directions. There is a net movement of water toward the inside of the thistle tube, where there is a higher solute (and lower water) concentration. **c.** Due to the incoming water molecules, the level of the solution rises in the thistle tube.

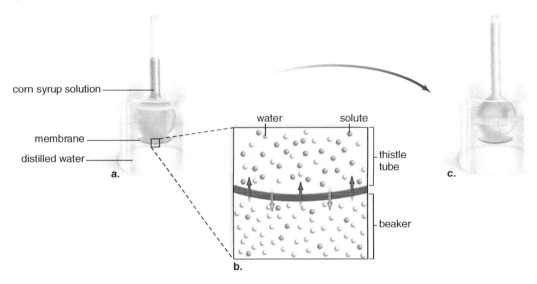

Tonicity

Tonicity is the relative concentration of solute (particles), and therefore also of solvent (water), outside the cell compared with inside the cell.

- An **isotonic solution** has the same concentration of solute (and therefore of water) as the cell. When cells are placed in an isotonic solution, there is no net movement of water (see Fig. 4.9a).

- A **hypertonic solution** has a higher solute (therefore, lower water) concentration than the cell. When cells are placed in a hypertonic solution, water moves out of the cell into the solution (see Fig. 4.9b).
- A **hypotonic solution** has a lower solute (therefore, higher water) concentration than the cell. When cells are placed in a hypotonic solution, water moves from the solution into the cell (see Fig.4.9c).

Red Blood Cells (Animal Cells)

A solution of 0.9% NaCl is isotonic to red blood cells. In such a solution, red blood cells maintain their normal appearance (Fig. 4.9a). A solution greater than 0.9% NaCl is hypertonic to red blood cells. In such a solution, the cells shrivel up, a process called **crenation** (Fig. 4.9b). A solution of less than 0.9% NaCl is hypotonic to red blood cells. In such a solution, the cells swell to bursting, a process called **hemolysis** (Fig. 4.9c).

Figure 4.9   Tonicity and red blood cells.

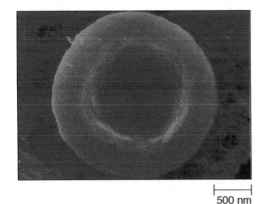 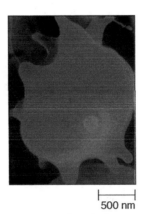 

500 nm	500 nm	500 nm

a. Isotonic solution. Red blood cell has normal appearance due to no net gain or loss of water.

b. Hypertonic solution. Red blood cell shrivels due to loss of water.

c. Hypotonic solution. Red blood cell fills to bursting due to gain of water.

Experimental Procedure: Demonstration of Tonicity in Red Blood Cells

Three stoppered test tubes on display have the following contents:
    Tube 1: 0.9% NaCl plus a few drops of whole sheep blood
    Tube 2: 10% NaCl plus a few drops of whole sheep blood
    Tube 3: 0.9% NaCl *plus distilled water* and a few drops of whole sheep blood

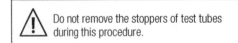

Do not remove the stoppers of test tubes during this procedure.

1. In the second column of Table 4.4, record the tonicity of each tube in relation to red blood cells.
2. Hold each tube in front of one of the pages of your lab manual. Determine whether you can see the print on the page through the tube. Record your findings in the third column of Table 4.4.

Table 4.4 Tonicity and Print Visibility			
Tube	Tonicity	Print Visibility	Explanation
1			
2			
3			

Conclusion: Tonicity and Print Visibility

- Explain in the fourth column of Table 4.4 why you can or cannot see the print.

Elodea (Plant Cells)

When plant cells are in a hypotonic solution, the large central vacuole gains water and exerts pressure, called **turgor pressure.** The cytoplasm, including the chloroplasts, is pushed up against the cell wall (Fig. 4.10a).

When plant cells are in a hypertonic solution, the central vacuole loses water, and the cytoplasm, including the chloroplasts, pulls away from the cell wall. This is called **plasmolysis** (Fig. 4.10b).

Figure 4.10 Elodea cells.
a. Surface view of cells in a hypotonic solution (above) and longitudinal section diagram (below). The large central vacuole, filled with water, pushes the cytoplasm, including the chloroplasts, right up against the cell wall. **b.** Surface view of cells in a hypertonic solution (above) and longitudinal section diagram (below). When the central vacuole loses water, cytoplasm, including the chloroplasts, piles up in the center of the cell because the cytoplasm has pulled away from the cell wall. (a: Magnification 400×)

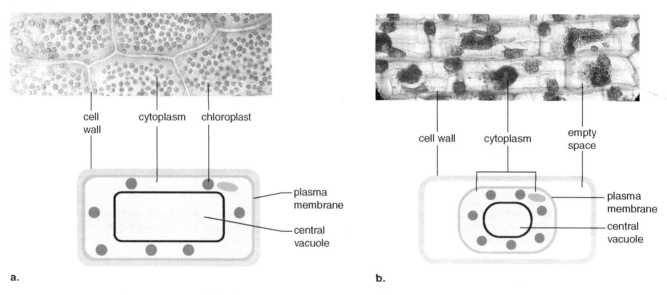

a.

b.

Experimental Procedure: Elodea Cells

Hypotonic Solution

1. If possible, use the *Elodea* slide you prepared earlier in this laboratory. If not, prepare a new wet mount of a small *Elodea* leaf using fresh water.
2. After several minutes, focus on the surface of the cells, and compare your slide with Figure 4.10a.
3. Complete the portion of Table 4.5 that pertains to a hypotonic solution.

Hypertonic Solution

1. Prepare a new wet mount of a small *Elodea* leaf using a 10% NaCl solution.
2. After several minutes, focus on the surface of the cells, and compare your slide with Figure 4.10b.
3. Complete the portion of Table 4.5 that pertains to a hypertonic solution.

Table 4.5 Effect of Tonicity on *Elodea* Cells

Tonicity	Appearance of Cells	Due to (Scientific Term)
Hypotonic		
Hypertonic		

Conclusions: Hypotonic and Hypertonic Solutions

- In a hypotonic solution, the large central vacuole of plant cells exerts _____ pressure, and the chloroplasts are seen _____ the cell wall.
- In a hypertonic solution, the central vacuole loses water, and the cytoplasm including the chloroplasts have _____ the cell wall.

Experimental Procedure: Potato Strips

(This experimental procedure runs for one hour. Prior setup can maximize time efficiency.)

1. Cut two strips of potato, each about 7 cm long and 1.5 cm wide.
2. Label two test tubes 1 and 2. Place one *potato strip* in each tube.
3. Fill tube 1 with *water* to cover the potato strip.
4. Fill tube 2 with 10% *sodium chloride* (NaCl) to cover the potato strip.
5. After 1 hour, remove the potato strips from the test tubes and place them on a paper towel. Observe each strip for limpness (water loss) or stiffness (water gain). Which tube has the limp potato strip?

   _____ Why did water diffuse out of the potato strip in this tube?

   _____

   Which tube has the stiff potato strip? _____ Why did water diffuse into the potato strip in this tube? _____

4.5   pH and Cells

The pH of a solution tells its hydrogen ion concentration [H^+]. The **pH scale** ranges from 0 to 14. A pH of 7 is neutral (Fig. 4.11). A pH lower than 7 indicates that the solution is acidic (has more hydrogen ions than hydroxide ions), whereas a pH greater than 7 indicates that the solution is basic (has more hydroxide ions than hydrogen ions). A **buffer** is a system of chemicals that takes up excess hydrogen ions or hydroxide ions, as appropriate.

The concept of pH is important in biology because living organisms are very sensitive to hydrogen ion concentration. For example, in humans the pH of the blood must be maintained at about 7.4 or we become ill. All living things need to maintain the hydrogen ion concentration, or pH, at a constant level.

Why are cells and organisms buffered? _____

Figure 4.11   The pH scale.
The proportionate amount of hydrogen ions (H^+) to hydroxide ions (OH^-) is indicated by the diagonal line.

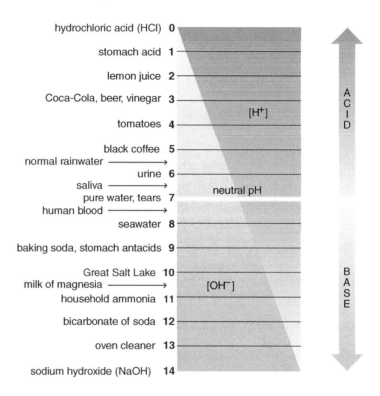

Experimental Procedure: pH and Cells

1. Label three test tubes, and fill them to the halfway mark as follows: tube 1: *water;* tube 2: *buffer* (inorganic) solution; and tube 3: *simulated cytoplasm* (buffered protein solution).
2. Use pH paper to determine the pH of each tube. Dip the end of a stirring rod into the solution, and then touch the stirring rod to a 5 cm strip of pH paper. Read the current pH by matching the color observed with the color code on the pH paper package. Record your results in the "pH Before Acid" column in Table 4.6.
3. Add 0.1 N hydrochloric acid (HCl) dropwise to each tube until you have added 5 drops—shake or swirl after each drop. Use pH paper as in step 2 to determine the new pH of each solution. Record your results in the "pH After Acid" column in Table 4.6.

> ⚠ **Hydrochloric acid (HCl)** used to produce an acid pH is a strong, caustic acid. Exercise care in using this chemical. If any HCl spills on your skin, rinse immediately with clear water. Follow your instructor's directions for disposal of tubes that contain HCl.

Table 4.6 pH and Cells

Tube	Contents	pH Before Acid	pH After Acid	Explanation
1	Water			
2	Buffer			
3	Cytoplasm			

Conclusions: pH and Cells

- Enter your explanations in the last column of Table 4.6.
- Why would you expect cytoplasm to be as effective as the buffer in maintaining pH?_____

_____

Experimental Procedure: Effectiveness of Antacids

Perform this procedure to test the ability of commercial products such as Alka-Seltzer, Rolaids, Tums, or antacid tablets to absorb excess H^+.

1. Use a mortar and pestle to grind up the amount of *antacid* that is listed as one dose.
2. For each antacid tested, use a 100 ml of *phenol red solution* diluted to a faint pink to wash the antacid into a 250 ml beaker. Phenol red solution is a pH indicator that turns yellow in an acid and red in a base. Use a stirring rod to get the powder to dissolve.
3. Add and count the number of *0.1 N HCl drops* it takes for the solution to turn light yellow.
4. Record your results in Table 4.7.

Table 4.7 Effectiveness of Antacids

Antacid	Drops of Acid Needed to Reach End Point	Evaluation
1		
2		
3		

Conclusions: Effectiveness of Antacids

- Participate with others in concluding which of the antacids tested neutralizes the most acid.

_____

- Did dosage in mg have any effect on the results?_____

_____

- Which of the substances on the label could be a buffer?_____

Laboratory Review 4

1. What characteristics do all eukaryotic cells have in common? _____

   _____

2. Some white blood cells are said to be amoeboid. How do you predict that these cells move?

   _____

3. Why would you predict that an animal cell, but not a plant cell, might burst when placed in a hypotonic

   solution? _____

   _____

4. Which of the cellular organelles would be included in a category called:

   a. Membranous canals and vacuoles? _____

   _____

   b. Energy-related organelles? _____

   _____

5. How do you distinguish between rough endoplasmic reticulum and smooth endoplasmic reticulum?

   a. Structure _____

   b. Function _____

6. If a dialysis bag filled with water is placed in a molasses solution, what do you predict will happen to

   the weight of the bag over time? _____

   Why? _____

   _____

7. What is the relationship between plant cell structure and the ability of plants to stand upright?

   _____

   _____

8. The police are trying to determine if material removed from the scene of a crime was plant matter. What

   would you suggest they microscopically look for? _____

   _____

9. A test tube contains red blood cells and a salt solution. When the tube is held up to a page, you can see

   the print. With reference to a concentration of 0.9% sodium chloride (NaCl), how concentrated is the

   salt solution? _____

10. Predict the microscopic appearance of cells in the leaf tissue of a wilted plant. _____

   _____

***Biology* Website**

The companion website for *Biology* provides a wealth of
information organized and integrated by chapter. You will find
practice tests, animations, videos, and much more that will
complement your learning and understanding of general
biology.

www.mhhe.com/maderbiology10

McGraw-Hill Access Science Website

An Encyclopedia of Science and Technology Online
which provides more information including videos
that can enhance the laboratory experience.

www.accessscience.com

5

How Enzymes Function

Learning Outcomes

Introduction

The cell carries out many chemical reactions. All the chemical reactions that occur in a cell are collectively called **metabolism.** A possible chemical reaction can be indicated like this:

$$\underset{\text{reactants}}{A + B} \longrightarrow \underset{\text{products}}{C + D}$$

In all chemical reactions, the **reactants** are molecules that undergo a change, which results in the **products.** The arrow stands for the change that produced the product(s). The number of reactants and products can vary; in the one you are studying today, a single reactant breaks down to two products. All the reactions that occur in a cell have an enzyme. **Enzymes** are organic catalysts that speed metabolic reactions. Because enzymes are specific and speed only one type of reaction, they are given names. In today's laboratory, you will be studying the action of the enzyme **catalase.** The reactants in an enzymatic chemical reaction are called **substrate(s)** (Fig. 5.1).

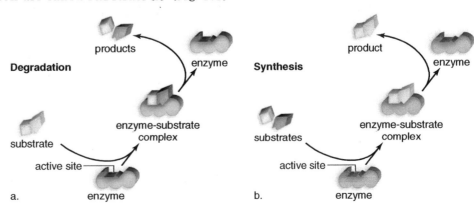

Figure 5.1   Enzymatic action.
The reaction occurs on the surface of the enzyme at the active site. The enzyme is reusable. **a.** Substrate is broken down. **b.** Substrates are combined.

Enzymes are specific because they have a shape that accommodates the shape of their substrates. Enzymatic reactions can be indicated like this:

$$E + S \longrightarrow ES \longrightarrow E + P$$

In this reaction, E = enzyme, ES = enzyme-substrate complex, and P = product.

Two types of enzymatic reactions common to cells are shown in Figure 5.1. During degradation reactions, the substrate is broken down to the product(s), and during synthesis reactions, the substrates are joined to form a product. The location where the enzyme and substrate form an enzyme-substrate complex is called the **active site** because the reaction occurs here. At the end of the reaction, the product is released, and the enzyme can then combine with the substrate again. A cell needs only a small amount of an enzyme because enzymes are used over and over. Some enzymes have turnover rates well in excess of a million product molecules per minute.

5.1 Catalase Activity

Catalase is involved in a degradation reaction: Catalase speeds the breakdown of hydrogen peroxide (H_2O_2) in nearly all organisms including bacteria, plants, and animals. A cellular organelle called a peroxisome, which contains catalase, is present in every plant and animal organ. This means that we could use any plant or animal organ as our source of catalase today. Commonly, school laboratories use the potato as a source of catalase because potatoes are easily obtained and cut up.

Catalase performs a useful function in organisms because hydrogen peroxide is harmful to cells. Hydrogen peroxide is a powerful oxidizer that can attack and denature cellular molecules like DNA! Knowing its harmful nature, humans use hydrogen peroxide as a commercial antiseptic to kill germs. In reduced concentration, hydrogen peroxide is a whitening agent used to bleach hair and teeth. Skillful technicians use it to provide oxygen to aquatic plants and fish, but it is also used industrially to clean most anything from tubs to sewage. It's even put in glow sticks where it reacts with a dye that then emits light!

Experimental Procedure: Catalase Activity

Catalase speeds the breakdown of hydrogen peroxide to water and oxygen:

$$2\ H_2O_2 \xrightarrow{\text{catalase}} 2\ H_2O + O_2$$
$$\text{hydrogen peroxide} \qquad \text{water} \quad \text{oxygen}$$

What is the reactant in this reaction? _____ What is the substrate for catalase? _____

What are the products in this reaction? _____ and _____ Bubbling occurs as the reaction proceeds. Why? _____

With a wax pencil, label and mark three clean test tubes at the 1 cm and 5 cm levels.

Tube 1   1. Fill to the first mark with *catalase* buffered at pH 7.0, the optimum pH for catalase.
         2. Fill to the second mark with *hydrogen peroxide*. Swirl well to mix, and wait at least
             20 seconds for bubbling to develop.
         3. Measure the height of the bubble column (in millimeters), and record your results
             in Table 5.1.

Tube 2   1. Fill to the first mark with *water*.
         2. Fill to the second mark with *hydrogen peroxide*. Swirl well to mix, and wait at least
             20 seconds.
         3. Measure the height of the bubble column (in millimeters), and record your results
             in Table 5.1.

Tube 3   1. Fill to the first mark with *catalase*.
         2. Fill to the second mark with *sucrose solution*. Swirl well to mix; wait 20 seconds.
         3. Measure the height of the bubble column, and record your results in Table 5.1.

Table 5.1	Catalase Activity		
Tube	**Contents**	**Bubble Column Height**	**Explanation**
1	Catalase Hydrogen peroxide		
2	Water Hydrogen peroxide		
3	Catalase Sucrose solution		

Conclusions: Catalase Activity

- Which tube showed the bubbling you expected? _____ Conclude why this tube showed
  bubbling, and record your explanation in Table 5.1.

- Which tube is a control? _____ If this tube showed bubbling, what could you conclude about
  your procedure? _____ Record an explanation for the results in Table 5.1.

- Enzymes are specific; they speed only a reaction that contains their substrate. Which tube exemplifies
  this characteristic of an enzyme? _____ Record your explanation for the results in Table 5.1.

5.2   Effect of Temperature on Enzyme Activity

In general, cold temperatures slow chemical reactions, and warm temperatures speed chemical reactions.
Boiling, however, causes an enzyme to **denature** altering its normal shape in a way that inactivates it.

Experimental Procedure: Effect of Temperature

With a wax pencil, label and mark three clean test tubes at the 1 cm and 5 cm levels.

1. Fill each tube to the first mark with *catalase* buffered at pH 7.0, the optimum pH for catalase.
2. Place tube 1 in a refrigerator or cold water bath, tube 2 in an incubator or warm water bath, and
    tube 3 in a boiling water bath. Complete the second column in Table 5.2. Wait 15 minutes.

3. As soon as you remove the tubes one at a time from the refrigerator, incubator, and boiling water, fill to the second mark with *hydrogen peroxide.*
4. Swirl well to mix, and wait 20 seconds.
5. Measure the height of the bubble column (in millimeters) in each tube, and record your results in Table 5.2.
6. Plot your results in Figure 5.2. Put temperature (°C) on the X-axis and bubble column height (mm) on the Y-axis.

Table 5.2 Effect of Temperature

Tube	Temperature °C	Bubble Column Height (mm)	Explanation
1 Refrigerator			
2 Incubator			
3 Boiling water			

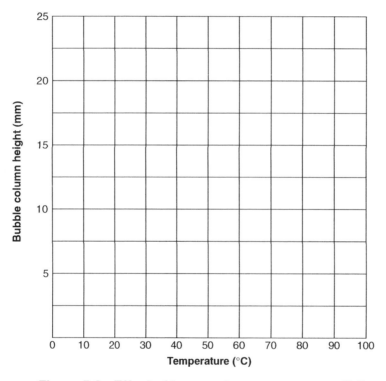

Figure 5.2   Effect of temperature on enzyme activity.

Conclusions: Effect of Temperature

- The amount of bubbling corresponds to the degree of enzyme activity. Explain in Table 5.2 the degree of enzyme activity per tube.
- What is your conclusion concerning the effect of temperature on enzyme activity?

5.3 Effect of Concentration on Enzyme Activity

In general, a higher enzyme or substrate concentration results in faster enzyme activity—that is, the amount of product per unit time for any particular reaction will increase.

Experimental Procedure: Effect of Enzyme Concentration

With a wax pencil, label three clean test tubes.

Tube 1
1. Mark this tube at the 1 cm and 5 cm levels.
2. Fill to the first mark with buffered *catalase* and to the second mark with *hydrogen peroxide*.
3. Swirl well to mix, and wait 20 seconds.
4. Measure the height of the bubble column (in millimeters), and record your results in Table 5.3.

Tube 2
1. Mark this tube at the 2 cm and 6 cm levels.
2. Fill to the first mark with buffered *catalase* and to the second mark with *hydrogen peroxide*.
3. Swirl well to mix, and wait 20 seconds.
4. Measure the height of the bubble column (in millimeters), and record your results in Table 5.3.

Tube 3
1. Mark this tube at the 3 cm and 7 cm levels.
2. Fill to the first mark with buffered *catalase* and to the second mark with *hydrogen peroxide*.
3. Swirl well to mix, and wait 20 seconds.
4. Measure the height of the bubble column (in millimeters), and record your results in Table 5.3.

Table 5.3 Effect of Enzyme Concentration

Tube	Amount of Enzyme	Bubble Column Height (mm)	Explanation
1	1 cm		
2	2 cm		
3	3 cm		

Conclusions : Effect of Concentration

- The amount of bubbling corresponds to the degree of enzyme activity. Explain in Table 5.3 the degree of enzyme activity per tube.

- If unlimited time was allotted, would the results be the same in all tubes? _____ Explain why or why not._____

- Would you expect similar results if the substrate concentration were varied in the same manner as the enzyme concentration? _____ Why or why not? _____

- What is your conclusion concerning the effect of concentration on enzyme activity? _____ _____

5.4 Effect of pH on Enzyme Activity

Each enzyme has a pH at which the speed of the reaction is optimum (occurs best). Any higher or lower pH affects hydrogen bonding and the structure of the enzyme, leading to reduced activity.

⚠️ **Hydrochloric acid (HCl)** used to produce an acid pH is a strong, caustic acid, and sodium hydroxide (NaOH) used to produce a basic pH is a strong, caustic base. Exercise care in using these chemicals, and follow your instructor's directions for disposal of tubes that contain these chemicals. If any acidic or basic solutions spill on your skin, rinse immediately with clear water.

Experimental Procedure: Effect of pH

With a wax pencil, label and mark three clean test tubes at the 1 cm, 3 cm, and 7 cm levels. Fill each tube to the 1 cm level with nonbuffered *catalase*.

Tube 1
1. Fill to the second mark with *water* adjusted to pH 3 by the addition of *HCl*.
2. Fill to the third mark with *hydrogen peroxide*. Wait one minute.
3. Swirl to mix, and wait 20 seconds.
4. Measure the height of the bubble column (in millimeters), and record your results in Table 5.4.

Tube 2
1. Fill to the second mark with *water* adjusted to pH 7.
2. Wait one minute. Fill to the third mark with *hydrogen peroxide*.
3. Swirl to mix, and wait 20 seconds.
4. Measure the height of the bubble column (in millimeters), and record your results in Table 5.4.

Tube 3
1. Fill to the second mark with *water* adjusted to pH 11 by the addition of *NaOH*.
2. Fill to the third mark with *hydrogen peroxide*. Wait one minute.
3. Swirl to mix, and wait 20 seconds.
4. Measure the height of the bubble column (in millimeters), and record your results in Table 5.4.
5. Plot your results in Figure 5.3. Put pH on the X-axis and bubble column height (mm) on the Y-axis.

Table 5.4   Effect of pH

Tube	pH	Bubble Column Height (mm)	Explanation
1	3		
2	7		
3	11		

Figure 5.3   Effect of pH on enzyme activity.

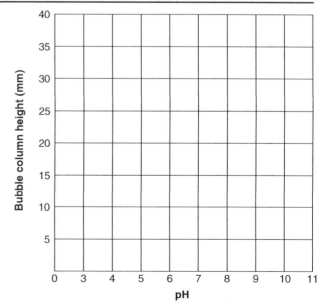

Conclusions : Effect of pH

- The amount of bubbling corresponds to the degree of enzyme activity. Explain in Table 5.4 the degree of enzyme activity per tube.
- The results of which tube in Table 5.1 could be used as a control for Table 5.4? _____

  Why could this tube be considered a control? _____

- What is your conclusion concerning the effect of pH on enzyme activity? _____

  _____

Factors That Affect Enzyme Activity

In Table 5.5, summarize what you have learned about factors that affect the speed of an enzymatic reaction. For example, in general, what type of temperature promotes enzyme activity, and what type inhibits enzyme activity? Answer similarly for enzyme or substrate concentration and pH.

Table 5.5 Factors That Affect Enzyme Activity		
Factors	**Promote Enzyme Activity**	**Inhibit Enzyme Activity**
Temperature		
Enzyme or substrate concentration		
pH		

Conclusions : Factors That Affect Enzyme Activity

- Why does a warm temperature promote enzyme activity? _____

  _____

- Why does increasing enzyme concentration promote enzyme activity? _____

  _____

- Why does optimum pH promote enzyme activity? _____

  _____

Laboratory Review 5

1. What happens at the active site of an enzyme? _____

_____

2. On the basis of the active site, explain why the following conditions speed a chemical reaction:

   a. More enzyme _____

   b. More substrate _____

3. Name three other conditions (other than the ones mentioned in question 2) that maximize enzymatic reactions.

   a. _____   b. _____   c. _____

4. Explain the necessity for each of the three conditions you listed in question 3.

   a. _____

   b. _____

   c. _____

5. Lipase is a digestive enzyme that digests fat droplets in the basic conditions ($NaHCO_3$ is present) of the small intestine. Indicate which of the following test tubes would show digestion following incubation at 37°C, and explain why the others would not.

   Tube 1: Water, fat droplets _____

   Tube 2: Water, fat droplets, lipase _____

   Tube 3: Water, fat droplets, lipase, $NaHCO_3$ _____

   Tube 4: Water, lipase, $NaHCO_3$ _____

6. Fats are digested to fatty acids and glycerol. As the reaction described in question 5 proceeds, the solution will become what type pH? _____ Why? _____

_____

7. Given the following reaction:

$$2 \ H_2O_2 \xrightarrow{\text{catalase}} 2 \ H_2O + O_2$$

hydrogen   water   oxygen
peroxide

   a. Which substance is the substrate? _____

   b. Which substance is the enzyme? _____

   c. Which substances are the end products? _____

   d. Is this a synthetic or degradative reaction? _____ .

6
Photosynthesis

Learning Outcomes

Introduction

The simplified overall equation for **photosynthesis** is

$$CO_2 + H_2O \xrightarrow{\text{solar energy}} (CH_2O) + O_2$$

In this equation, (CH_2O) represents any general carbohydrate. Sometimes, this equation is multiplied by 6 so that glucose $(C_6H_{12}O_6)$ appears as an end product of photosynthesis. Photosynthesis takes place in chloroplasts (Fig. 6.1). Here membranous thylakoids are stacked in grana surrounded by the stroma. During the light reactions, pigments within the *thylakoid* membranes absorb solar energy, water is split, and oxygen is released. The Calvin cycle reactions occur within the *stroma*. During these reactions, carbon dioxide (CO_2) is reduced to a carbohydrate (CH_2O).

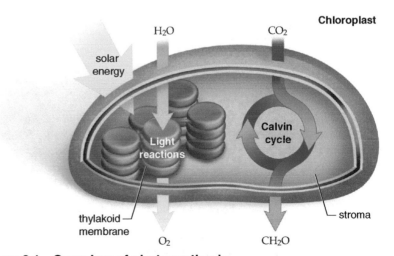

Figure 6.1 Overview of photosynthesis.
Photosynthesis includes the light reactions when energy is collected and O_2 is released and the Calvin cycle reactions when CO_2 is reduced and carbohydrate (CH_2O) is formed.

6.1 Photosynthetic Pigments

Later is this laboratory, we will learn that visible (white) light is composed of different colors of light and that pigments are specialized to absorb a particular color of light. We can, therefore, hypothesize that leaves contain various pigments allowing them to make use of a significant portion of white light for photosynthesis. Restate this hypothesis here:

Hypothesis: _____

To support this hypothesis, we will use a technique called chromatography to separate the pigments found in leaves. Chromatography separates molecules from each other on the basis of their solubility in particular solvents. The solvents used in the following Experimental Procedure are petroleum ether and acetone, which have no charged groups and are therefore nonpolar. As a nonpolar solvent moves up the chromatography paper, the pigment moves along with it. The more nonpolar a pigment, the more soluble it is in a nonpolar solvent and the faster and farther it proceeds up the chromatography paper.

Experimental Procedure: Photosynthetic Pigments

1. Assemble a chromatography apparatus (large, dry test tube and cork with a hook) and a strip of precut chromatography paper (handle by the top only) (Fig. 6.2). Attach the paper strip to the hook, and test for fit. The paper should hang straight and barely touch the bottom of the test tube; trim if necessary. Measure 2 cm from the bottom of the paper, and place a small dot with a pencil (not a pen). With a wax pencil, mark the test tube 1 cm below where the dot is with the stopper in place. Set the apparatus in a test tube rack.

2. Prepare (or obtain) a *pigment extract,* as directed by your instructor.

> ⚠ **Ether** (which is part of the chromatography solution) is toxic and extremely flammable. Do not breathe the fumes, and do not place the chromatography solution near any source of heat. A fume (ventilation) hood is recommended.

Figure 6.2 Paper chromatography.

The paper must be cut to size and arranged to hang down without touching the sides of a dry tube. Then the pigment (chlorophyll) solution is applied to a designated spot. The chromatogram develops after the spotted paper is suspended in the chromatography solution.

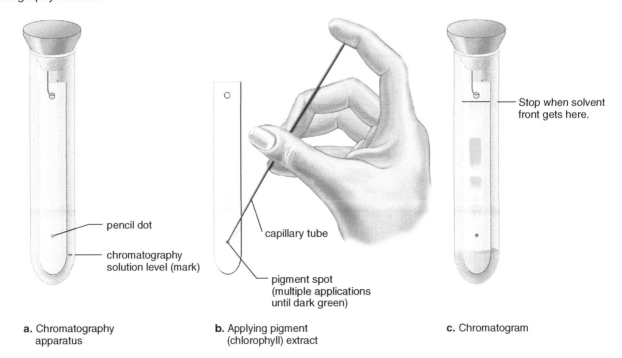

a. Chromatography apparatus — pencil dot — chromatography solution level (mark)

b. Applying pigment (chlorophyll) extract — capillary tube — pigment spot (multiple applications until dark green)

c. Chromatogram — Stop when solvent front gets here.

3. Place the premarked chromatography paper strip onto a paper towel.
4. Fill a capillary tube by placing it into the extract. (It will fill by its own capillary action.)
5. Repeatedly apply the *pigment extract* to the pencil dot on the chromatographic strip. Let the spot dry between each application. Try to obtain a small dark green spot. (Placing your index finger over the wide end of the capillary tube will help keep the dot small.)
6. In a **fume hood,** add *chromatography solution* to the mark you made earlier. Do not submerge the pigment spot. Set the apparatus in a test tube rack and close the chromatography apparatus tightly. Do not shake the test tube during the chromatography.
7. Allow approximately 10 minutes for your chromatogram to develop, but check it frequently so that the pigments do not reach the top of the paper.
8. When the solvent has moved to within 1 cm of the upper edge of the paper (Fig. 6.2c), remove your chromatogram. Close the apparatus tightly. With a pencil, lightly mark the location of the solvent front (where the solvent stopped) and allow the chromatogram to dry in the fume hood.
9. Notice the different pigment bands. **Carotenes** are represented by the yellow band at the top. **Xanthophylls** are yellow-orange and may be represented in multiple bands. The blue-green band is **chlorophyll *a*,** and the lowest, yellow-green band is **chlorophyll *b*.**
10. Measure the distance in mm from the initial pigment spot to the top of each individual pigment band, and record these values in Table 6.1. Measure the distance the solvent moved from the initial pigment spot to the solvent front. Use this formula to calculate the R_f (ratio-factor) values for each pigment, and record these values in Table 6.1:

$$R_f = \frac{\text{distance moved by pigment}}{\text{distance moved by solvent}}$$

Table 6.1 R_f (Ratio-Factor) Values for Each Pigment		
Pigments	**Distance Moved (mm)**	**R_f Values**
Carotenes		
Xanthophylls		
Chlorophyll *a*		
Chlorophyll *b*		
Solvent		– – – –

Conclusions: Photosynthetic Pigments

- Do your results support the hypothesis that plant leaves contain various photosynthetic pigments?

Explain. _____

6.2 Solar Energy

During light reactions of photosynthesis solar energy is absorbed by the photosynthetic pigments and is transformed into the chemical energy of a carbohydrate (CH_2O). Without solar energy, photosynthesis would be impossible.

Verify that photosynthesis releases oxygen by reviewing the overall equation for photosynthesis on page 65. Release of oxygen from a plant indicates that the light reactions of photosynthesis are occurring. The oxygen released during photosynthesis is taken up by a plant when cellular respiration occurs. This must be taken into account when the rate of photosynthesis is calculated.

Role of White Light

White (sun) light contains different colors of light, as is demonstrated when white light passes through a prism (Fig. 6.3). White light is the best for photosynthesis because it contains all the colors of light.

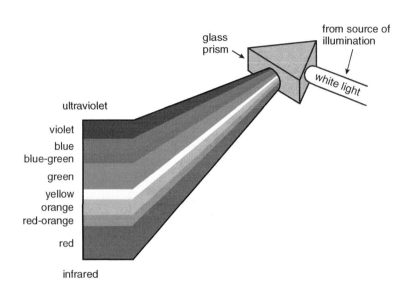

Figure 6.3 White light.
White light is made up of various colors, as can be seen when white light passes through a prism.

Experimental Procedure: White Light

1. Place a generous quantity of *Elodea* with the cut end up (make sure the cuts are fresh) in a test tube with a rubber stopper containing a piece of glass tubing, as illustrated in Figure 6.4. When assembled, this is your volumeter for studying the need for light in photosynthesis. (Do not hold the volumeter in your hand, as body heat will also drive the reaction forward.) Your instructor will show you how to fix the volumeter in an upright position.

2. Before stoppering the test tube, add sufficient 3% *sodium bicarbonate* ($NaHCO_3$) solution so that, when the rubber stopper is inserted into the tube, the solution comes to rest at about 1/4 the length of the upright glass tubing. Mark this location on the glass tubing with a wax pencil.

3. Place a beaker of plain water next to the *Elodea* tube to serve as a heat absorber. Place a lamp (150 watt) next to the beaker. The tube, beaker, and lamp should be as close to one another as possible.

4. Turn on the lamp. As soon as the edge of the solution in the tubing begins to move, time the reaction for 10 minutes. Be careful not to bump the tubing or to readjust the stopper, or your readings will be altered. After 10 minutes, mark the edge of the solution, and measure

   in millimeters the distance the edge moved upward: _____ mm/10 min. This is **net**

   photosynthesis, a measurement that does not take into account the oxygen that was used up for

   cellular respiration. Record your results in Table 6.2. Why did the edge move upward? _____

Figure 6.4 Volumeter.
A volumeter apparatus is used to study the role of light in photosynthesis.

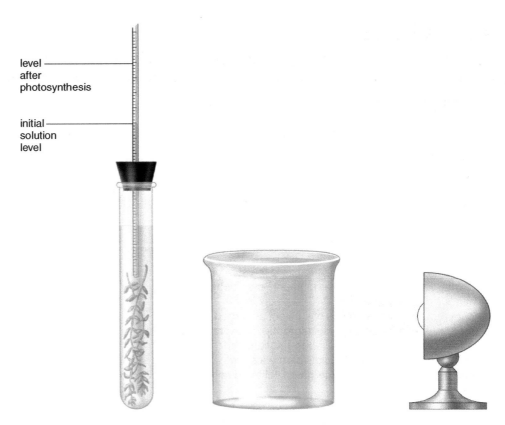

level after photosynthesis

initial solution level

5. Carefully wrap the tube containing *Elodea* in aluminum foil, and record here the length of time it takes for the edge of the solution in the tubing to move downward 1 mm: _____. Convert your measurement to _____ mm/10 min, and record this value for **cellular respiration** in Table 6.2. (Do not use a minus sign, even though the edge moved downward.) Why does cellular respiration, which occurs in a plant all the time, cause the edge to move downward? _____

_____

6. If the *Elodea* had not been respiring in step 4, how far would the edge have moved upward? _____ mm/10 min. This is **gross photosynthesis** (net photosynthesis + cellular respiration). Record this number in Table 6.2.

7. Calculate the **rate of photosynthesis** (mm/hr) by multiplying gross photosynthesis (mm/10 min) by 6 (that is, 10 min × 6 = 60 min = 1 hr): _____ mm/hr. Record this value in Table 6.2.

Table 6.2 Rate of Photosynthesis (White Light)
Data
Net photosynthesis (white light) (mm/10 min)
Cellular respiration (no light) (mm/10 min)
Gross photosynthesis (net + cellular respiration) (mm/10 min)
Rate of photosynthesis (mm/hr)

Role of Green Light

Green light is only one part of white light (see Fig. 6.3). The photosynthetic pigments absorb certain colors of light better than other colors (Fig. 6.5). According to Figure 6.5, what color light do the chlorophylls absorb best? _____ Least? _____

What color light do the carotenoids (carotenes and xanthophylls) absorb best? _____ Least? _____

Hypothesize which color light is minimally utilized for photosynthesis. _____ The following Experimental Procedure will test your hypothesis.

Figure 6.5   Action spectrum for photosynthesis.
The action spectrum for photosynthesis is the sum of the absorption spectrums for the pigments chlorophyll *a*, chlorophyll *b*, and carotenoids. The peaks in this diagram represent wavelengths of sunlight absorbed by photosynthetic pigments. The chlorophylls absorb predominantly violet-blue and orange-red light and reflect green light. The carotenoids (carotenes and xanthophylls) absorb mostly blue-green light and reflect yellow-red light.

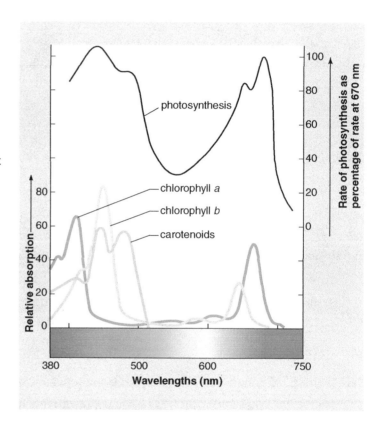

Experimental Procedure: Green Light

1. Add three drops of green dye (or use a green cellophane wrapper) to the beaker of water used in the previous Experimental Procedure until there is a distinctive green color. Remove all previous wax pencil marks from the glass tubing.
2. Record in Table 6.3 your data for gross photosynthesis (mm/10 min) and for rate of photosynthesis for white light (mm/hr) from Table 6.2.
3. Turn on the lamp. Mark the location of the edge of the solution on the glass tubing. As soon as the edge begins to move, time the reaction for 10 minutes. After 10 minutes, mark the edge of the solution, and measure in millimeters the distance the edge moved. Net photosynthesis for green light = _____ mm/10 min.
4. Carefully wrap the tube containing *Elodea* in aluminum foil, and record here the length of time it takes for the edge of the solution in the tubing to recede 1 mm: _____ . Convert your measurement to _____ mm/10 min.

5. Calculate gross photosynthesis for green light (mm/10 min) as you did for white light, and record your data in Table 6.3.

6. Calculate rate of photosynthesis for green light (mm/hr) as you did for white light, and record your data in Table 6.3.

7. Average and record the Table 6.3 class data for both white light and green light, and record these averages in Table 6.3.

8. The following equation shows the rate of photosynthesis (green light) as a percentage of the rate of photosynthesis (white light):

$$\text{Percentage} = \frac{\text{rate of photosynthesis (green light)}}{\text{rate of photosynthesis (white light)}} \times 100$$

This percentage, based on your data in Table 6.3, = _____. This percentage, based on class data in Table 6.3, = _____. Record these values in Table 6.3.

Table 6.3 Rate of Photosynthesis (Green Light)		
	Your Data	**Class Data**
Gross photosynthesis (mm/10 min)		
White (from Table 6.2)		
Green		
Rate of photosynthesis (mm/hr)		
White (from Table 6.2)		
Green		

Conclusions: Rate of Photosynthesis

- Do your results support the hypothesis that green light is minimally used by a land plant for photosynthesis? _____ Explain, with reference to Figure 6.5. _____

- How does the percentage based on your data differ from that based on class data?

6.3 Carbon Dioxide Uptake

During the Calvin cycle reactions of photosynthesis, the plant takes up carbon dioxide (CO_2) and reduces it to a carbohydrate, such as glucose ($C_6H_{12}O_6$). Therefore, the carbon dioxide in the solution surrounding *Elodea* should disappear as photosynthesis takes place.

Experimental Procedure: Carbon Dioxide Uptake

1. Temporarily remove the *Elodea* from the test tube. Empty the sodium bicarbonate ($NaHCO_3$) solution from the test tube, rinse the test tube thoroughly, and fill with a phenol red solution diluted to a faint pink. (Add more water if the solution is too dark.) Phenol red is a pH indicator that turns yellow in an acid and red in a base.

> ⚠️ **Phenol red** Avoid ingestion, inhalation, and contact with skin, eyes, and mucous membranes. Follow your instructor's directions for disposal of this chemical. Use protective eyewear when performing this experiment.

2. Blow *lightly* on the surface of the solution. Stop blowing as soon as the surface color changes to yellow. Then shake the test tube until the rest of the solution turns yellow.

   Blowing onto the solution adds what gas to the test tube? _____ When carbon dioxide combines with water, it forms carbonic acid. What causes the color change?

   _____

3. Thoroughly rinse the *Elodea* with distilled water, return it to the test tube with the phenol red solution, and assemble your volumeter as before.
4. The water in the beaker used to absorb heat should be clear.
5. Considering the test sample in Table 6.4, suggest a possible control sample for this experiment.

   _____

   If so directed, include a control sample in your experiment.
6. Turn on the lamp, and wait until the edge of the solution just begins to move upward. Note the time. Observe until you note a change in color. Record your results in Table 6.4.

7. Hypothesize why the solution in the test sample eventually turned red. _____

   _____

Table 6.4 Carbon Dioxide Uptake

Tube	Time for Color Change
Test sample: *Elodea* + phenol red solution + CO_2	
Control sample:	

6.4 The Light Reactions and the Calvin Cycle Reactions

Review the introduction to this laboratory. Note the overall equation for photosynthesis and that photosynthesis consists of the light reactions and the Calvin cycle reactions. Solar energy is absorbed by photosynthetic pigments during the light reactions and energy is used during the Calvin cycle reactions to reduce carbon dioxide to a carbohydrate.

Light Reactions

1. Photosynthetic pigments.

    a. What is the function of the photosynthetic pigments in photosynthesis? _____

    b. How does it benefit a plant to have a variety of photosynthetic pigments? (See Fig. 6.5.) _____

    _____

    c. Green light minimally promotes photosynthesis. Account for this observation with reference to

    the photosynthetic pigments. (See Fig. 6.5). _____

    d. Does this explain why leaves are green? _____ How so? _____
2. Water and oxygen.

    a. What happens to water during the light reactions? _____

    b. What happens to the released oxygen? _____
3. Location of the light reactions.

    Fill in the blank: The light reactions take place in the _____ membranes.
4. Summarize the light reactions based on this laboratory.

Calvin Cycle Reactions

1. Carbon dioxide and carbohydrate.

    What happens to carbon dioxide after it is taken up during the Calvin cycle reactions? _____

2. Location of the Calvin cycle reaction.

    Fill in the blank: The Calvin cycle reactions take place in the _____ .
3. Summarize the Calvin cycle reactions based on this laboratory.

Light Reactions and the Calvin Cycle Reactions

1. Examine the overall equation for photosynthesis and show that there is a relationship between the light reactions and the Calvin cycle reactions by drawing an arrow between the hydrogen atoms in water and the hydrogen atoms in the carbohydrate.

$$CO_2 + H_2O \longrightarrow (CH_2O) + O_2$$

2. Only because solar energy splits water can hydrogen atoms be used to reduce carbon dioxide. In this sense, solar energy is now stored in the carbohydrate.

Laboratory Review 6

1. How are plant pigments involved in photosynthesis? _____

   _____

2. Why is it beneficial to have several different plant pigments involved in photosynthesis? _____

   _____

3. On what basis does chromatography separate substances? _____

   _____

4. Some types of red algae carry on photosynthesis 70 meters beneath the ocean surface. What color light

   do you predict does not penetrate to this depth? _____

5. Consider the following reaction:

$$CO_2 + H_2O \longrightarrow \underset{\text{carbonic acid}}{H_2CO_3} \longrightarrow H^+ + HCO_3^-$$

   a. Phenol red, a pH indicator, turns yellow (indicating acid) when you breathe into a solution. How

   does the reaction explain why the solution turned acidic? _____

   _____

   b. Phenol red turns back to red when a plant in light is added to the solution. In terms of the reaction,

   why does this occur? _____

   _____

6. Gas exchange occurs in both photosynthesis and cellular respiration. Contrast these two processes by

   completing the following table:

	Organelle	Gas Given Off	Gas Taken Up
Photosynthesis			
Cellular respiration			

7. What experimental conditions were used in this laboratory to test for cellular respiration in

   plant cells? _____

8. Suppose you replaced *Elodea* with animal cells in the experimental test tube. Would the results differ

   according to the use of a white light or no light? _____ Explain. _____

   _____

Biology Website

The companion website for *Biology* provides a wealth of information organized and integrated by chapter. You will find practice tests, animations, videos, and much more that will complement your learning and understanding of general biology.

   www.mhhe.com/maderbiology10

McGraw-Hill Access Science Website

An Encyclopedia of Science and Technology Online which provides more information including videos that can enhance the laboratory experience.

   www.accessscience.com

7
Cellular Respiration

Learning Outcomes

Introduction
- Give the overall equation for fermentation and cellular respiration.   75–76
- Relate the utilization of oxygen to each process.   75–76
- Explain the relationship between these processes and ATP molecules.   75–76

7.1 Fermentation
- Describe and explain the fermentation experiment.   76–78
- Relate the overall equation for fermentation to the fermentation experiment.   76–78
- State and explain the effects of food source on fermentation by yeast.   77–78

7.2 Cellular Respiration
- Describe and explain the cellular respiration experiment.   79–81
- Relate the overall equation for cellular respiration to the cellular respiration experiment.   79–81
- State and explain the effects of germination and nongermination of soybeans on the results of the cellular respiration experiment.   80–81

Introduction

In this laboratory, you will study **ethanol fermentation,** which is an ATP-generating process. When an organism, such as yeast, breaks down glucose to ethanol and carbon dioxide, only 2 ATP result but the process is anaerobic and does not require oxygen (Fig. 7.1a). Fermentation occurs in the cytoplasm and mitochondria are not involved. This reaction represents yeast fermentation:

$$C_6H_{12}O_6 \longrightarrow 2\,CO_2 + 2\,C_2H_5OH + 2\,ATP$$

glucose   carbon   ethanol
dioxide

Figure 7.1   Production of ATP.
Cells typically have three ways
to produce ATP. Two methods of
fermentation are seen but only one
method of cellular respiration is
typical. In prokaryotes, complete
cellular respiration occurs in the
cytoplasm, while eukaryotes
begin cellular respiration in
the cytoplasm and complete it
inside mitochondria.

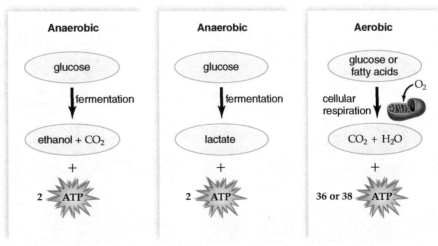

a. Yeast and some bacteria   b. Animals and some bacteria   c. Most organisms

When animals, such as humans, ferment, they produce lactate instead of ethanol and carbon dioxide (Fig.7.1*b*).

Following a study of yeast fermentation, you will study **cellular respiration** by germinating soybeans. Cellular respiration is an ATP-generating process that involves the complete breakdown of glucose or fatty acid to carbon dioxide and water. The process begins in the cytoplasm, but in eukaryotic cells, cellular respiration is completed in mitochondria. Cellular respiration is aerobic and requires oxygen, but it results in a buildup of 36 or 38 ATP (Fig. 7.1*c*). This equation represents cellular respiration:

$$C_6H_{12}O_6 + 6O_2 \longrightarrow 6CO_2 + 6H_2O + 36 \text{ or } 38 \text{ ATP}$$

glucose   oxygen   carbon   water
                          dioxide

7.1 Fermentation

When you study the ability of yeast to ferment sugar, you will need to use a respirometer to measure the amount of carbon dioxide given off. Your first experimental procedure shows you how to prepare your **respirometer.**

Experimental Procedure: Respirometer Practice

1. Completely fill a small tube (15 × 125 mm) with water (Fig. 7.2).
2. Invert a large tube (20 × 150 mm) over the small tube, and with your finger or a pencil, push the small tube up into the large tube until the upper lip of the small tube is in contact with the bottom of the large tube.
3. Quickly invert both tubes. Do not permit the small tube to slip away from the bottom of the large tube. A little water will leak out of the small tube and be replaced by an air bubble.
4. Practice this inversion until the bubble in the small tube is as small as you can make it.

Figure 7.2 Respirometer for fermentation.
Place a small tube inside a large tube. Hold the small tube in place as you rotate the entire apparatus, and an air bubble will form in the small tube.

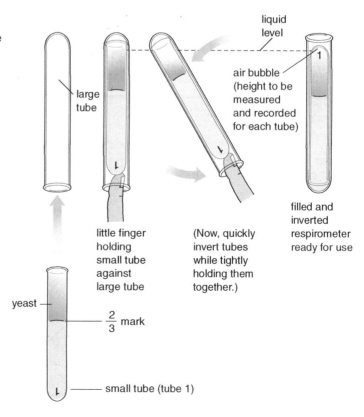

Ethanol Fermentation

Yeast fermentation to produce ethanol and carbon dioxide has long been utilized by humans to produce wine and bread. During the production of wine, it is the ethanol that is desired while bread and other baked goods rise when yeast gives off carbon dioxide (Fig. 7.3). Recently, there has been a great deal of interest in using ethanol produced by yeast fermentation of corn as a substitute for gasoline in cars.

Figure 7.3   Products of fermentation.

Testing Sugars

In the Experimental Procedure that follows, we are going to test which of several sugars is a better food source for yeast when they ferment. It will be assumed that the ease of sugar fermentation correlates with the amount of carbon dioxide given off within a certain time limit. As background data, observe the structure of the three sugars involved:

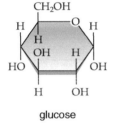

glucose   fructose   sucrose

State a hypothesis for your experiment in which you sequence the sugars according to how well you expect yeast to ferment them:

Hypothesis: _____

Experimental Procedure: Yeast Fermentation

Have four large test tubes ready. With a wax pencil, label and mark off a small test tube at the 2/3-full level. Use this tube to mark off three other small tubes at the same level.

1. Label and fill the small tubes as directed, and record the contents in Table 7.1.

   Tube 1   Fill to the mark with *glucose solution.*

   Tube 2   Fill to the mark with *fructose solution.*

   Tube 3   Fill to the mark with *sucrose solution.*

   Tube 4   Fill to the mark with *distilled water.*

2. Re-suspend a yeast solution each time, and fill all four tubes to the top with yeast suspension (Fig. 7.2).
3. Slide the large tubes over the small tubes, and invert them in the way you practiced. This will mix the yeast and sugar solutions.
4. Place the respirometers in a tube rack, and measure the initial height of the air space in the rounded bottom of the small tube. Record the height in Table 7.1.
5. Place the respirometers in an incubator or in a warm water bath maintained at 37°C. Note the time, and allow the respirometers to incubate about 20 minutes (incubator) or one hour (water bath). However, watch your respirometers and if they appear to be filling with gas quite rapidly, stop the incubation when appropriate. During the incubation period, begin the Experimental Procedure on cellular respiration (see page 79).
6. At the end of the incubation period, measure the final height of the gas bubble, and record it in Table 7.1. Calculate the net change, and record it in Table 7.1.

Table 7.1 Fermentation by Yeast

Tube	Sugar	Initial Gas Height	Final Gas Height	Net Change	Ease of Fermentation
1					
2					
3					
4					————————

Conclusions: Yeast Fermentation

- From your results, evaluate how the sugars tested compare as a food source for yeast fermentation. Enter your evaluation in Table 7.1.
- Do your data support or fail to support your hypothesis? _____
  Explain. _____
- Can your results be correlated with the comparative structure of the sugars? _____
  Explain. _____
- Which respirometer was the control? _____

7.2 Cellular Respiration

When germination occurs and plants begin to grow, cellular respiration can provide them with the ATP they need to produce all the molecules that allow them to grow. Consider, for example, Figure 7.4, which depicts soybean germination.

In the Experimental Procedure that follows, we are going to use oxygen uptake as evidence that germinating soybeans are carrying on cellular respiration. The need for oxygen by a germinating soybean will be compared to the need by nongerminating soybeans. State the hypothesis here:

Hypothesis: _____

Figure 7.4 Germination of a soybean seed.

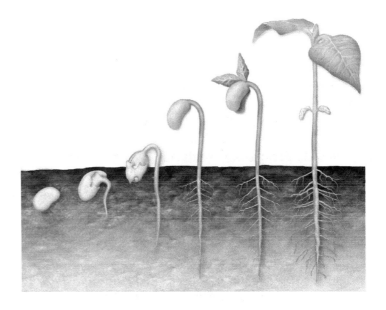

Experimental Procedure: Cellular Respiration

This Experimental Procedure uses potassium hydroxide (KOH) to remove carbon dioxide as it is given off. The equation for this reaction is:

$$CO_2 + 2\ KOH \longrightarrow \underset{\substack{\text{solid} \\ \text{potassium} \\ \text{carbonate}}}{K_2CO_3} + H_2O$$

> ⚠ **Potassium hydroxide (KOH)** is a strong, caustic base. Exercise care in using this chemical, and follow your instructor's directions for disposal of these tubes. If any potassium hydroxide should spill on your skin, rinse immediately with water.

1. Obtain a volumeter, an apparatus that measures changes in gas volumes. Remove the three vials from the volumeter. Remove the stoppers from the vials and the vials from the volumeter. Label the vials 1, 2, and 3.

Figure 7.5 Vials.
In this experiment, three vials are filled as noted.

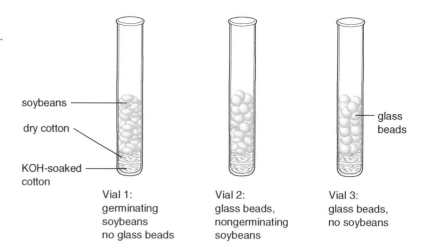

soybeans

dry cotton

KOH-soaked cotton

glass beads

Vial 1:
germinating
soybeans
no glass beads

Vial 2:
glass beads,
nongerminating
soybeans

Vial 3:
glass beads,
no soybeans

2. Using the same amounts, place a small wad of absorbent cotton in the bottom of each vial. Without getting the sides of the vials wet, use a dropper to saturate the cotton with 15% potassium hydroxide (KOH). Place a small wad of dry cotton on top of the KOH-soaked absorbent cotton (Fig. 7.5).

3. Count 25 germinating soybean seeds and add to vial 1. Count 25 dry (nongerminating) soybean seeds and add to vial 2. Add glass beads to vial 2 so that the volume occupied in vial 2 is approximately the same as in vial 1. Add only glass beads to vial 3 to bring to approximately the same volume.

4. Each stopper should have a vent (rubber tube) with a clamp and a graduated side arm. Remove the clamps from the vents. Adjust the graduated side arm until only about 5 mm to 1 cm protrudes through the stopper (Fig. 7.6).

5. With a dropper, add a drop of *Brodie manometer fluid* (or water colored with vegetable dye and a small amount of detergent) to each side arm.

6. Firmly place the stoppers in the vials. Adjust the stoppers until the side arms are parallel to the lab bench.

7. Adjust the location of the marker drop in the side arms with the assistance of a dry dropper in the vent. The marker drop of vial 3 (thermobarometer) should be in the middle of the side arm. The marker drop of vials 1 and 2 should be between 0.80 and 0.90 ml. Close the vent with the clamp when the marker drop is at the correct location.

8. Allow the respirometers to equilibrate for 5 minutes, and then record in Table 7.2, to the nearest 0.01 ml, the initial position of the marker drop in each graduated side arm.

9. Wait 10 minutes, and then record in Table 7.2 any change in the position of the marker drop. Wait 10 more minutes, and then record in Table 7.2 any change in the position of the marker drop. Then record in Table 7.2 the net change for each vial—that is, the initial reading for each vial minus the vial's 20-minute reading.

10. Did the marker drop change in vial 3 (glass beads)? _____ By how much? _____ Enter this number in the "Correction" column of Table 7.2, and use this number to correct the net change you observed in vials 1 and 2. (This is a correction for any change in volume due to atmospheric pressure changes or temperature changes.) This will complete Table 7.2.

Figure 7.6 Volumeter containing three respirometers.
In this experiment, the respirometers are vials filled as per Figure 7.5 with graduated side arms attached. Oxygen uptake is measured by movement of a marker drop in each side arm.

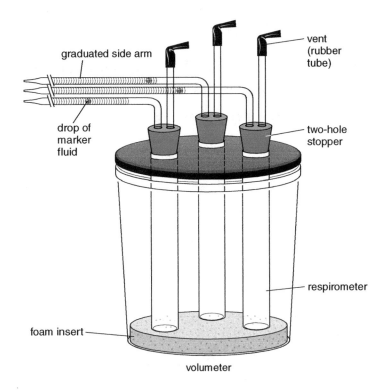

Table 7.2 Cellular Respiration							
Vial	Contents	Initial Reading	Reading After 10 Minutes	Reading After 20 Minutes	Net Change	Correction	(Corrected) Net Change
1	Germinating soybeans						
2	Dry (nongerminating) soybeans Glass beads						
3	Glass beads						

Conclusions: Cellular Respiration

- Do your results support or fail to support the hypothesis? _____

  Explain. _____

- Why was it necessary to absorb the carbon dioxide? _____

  _____

- Which respirometer in the soybean experiment was the control? _____

Laboratory Review 7

1. Both fermentation and cellular respiration ordinarily begin with what molecule? _____

2. How do the overall equations for these processes indicate that fermentation is anaerobic and that cellular respiration is aerobic? _____

   _____

3. Glucose breakdown results in the breaking of C—H bonds and stored energy is released. Contrast the end products of fermentation and cellular respiration in terms of their energy content. _____

   _____

4. Fermentation results in the net production of only 2 ATP, while cellular respiration results in the production of at least 36 ATP. Explain these results with reference to the end products of both of these processes. _____

   _____

5. In the Experimental Procedure: Yeast Fermentation, the gas bubble got larger. What gas was causing this increase in bubble size? _____

6. Why is it reasonable that, of the three sugars (glucose, fructose, and sucrose), glucose would result in the most activity during the fermentation experiment? _____

   _____

7. In the Experimental Procedure: Cellular Respiration, what gas was taken up by the soybeans? _____

8. Explain the role of each of the following components in the cellular respiration experiment:

   a. KOH _____

   b. Germinating soybeans _____

   c. Dry (nongerminating) soybeans _____

9. If you performed the cellular respiration experiment without soaking the cotton with KOH, what results would you predict? _____

   Why? _____

8

Mitosis and Meiosis

Learning Outcomes

8.1 The Cell Cycle
- Name and describe the stages of the cell cycle. 84
- Describe how the cell prepares for mitosis, and identify the phases of mitosis in models and microscopic slides. Explain how the chromosome number stays constant. 85–88
- Describe animal and plant cell cytokinesis. 89–90

8.2 Meiosis
- Name and describe the phases of meiosis I and meiosis II with attention to the movement of chromosomes. Explain how the chromosome number is reduced. 91–95

8.3 Mitosis Versus Meiosis
- Compare the effects of mitosis to meiosis. 96–97
- Contrast the behavior of chromosomes during mitosis with the behavior of chromosomes during meiosis I. Explain why meiosis I is emphasized and not meiosis II. 96–97

8.4 Karyotype Abnormalities
- Recognize that abnormalities in chromosome number and structure can occur when cells divide. 98

8.5 Gametogenesis in Animals
- Contrast spermatogenesis and oogenesis using models and slides. 99–101

Introduction

Dividing cells experience nuclear division, cytoplasmic division, and a period of time between divisions called interphase. During **interphase,** the nucleus appears normal, and the cell is performing its usual cellular functions. Also, the cell is increasing all of its components, including such organelles as the mitochondria, ribosomes, and centrioles, if present. DNA replication (making an exact copy of the DNA) occurs toward the end of interphase. Thereafter, the chromosomes, which contain DNA, are duplicated and contain two chromatids held together at a **centromere.** These chromatids are called **sister chromatids.**

During nuclear division, called **mitosis,** the new nuclei receive the same number of chromosomes as the parental nucleus. When the cytoplasm divides, a process called **cytokinesis,** two daughter cells are produced. In multicellular organisms, mitosis permits growth and repair of tissues. In eukaryotic, unicellular organisms, mitosis is a form of asexual reproduction. Sexually reproducing organisms utilize another form of nuclear division, called **meiosis.** In animals, meiosis is a part of gametogenesis, the production of gametes (sex cells). The gametes are sperm in male animals and eggs in female animals. As a result of meiosis, the daughter cells have half the number of chromosomes as the parental cell. As we shall see, meiosis contributes to recombination of genetic material and to diversity among sexually reproducing organisms.

This laboratory examines both mitotic and meiotic cell division to show their similarities and differences and it also discusses chromosome abnormalities that can occur during mitosis and meiosis.

8.1 The Cell Cycle

As stated in the Introduction, the period of time between cell divisions is known as interphase. Because early investigators noted little visible activity between cell divisions, they dismissed this period of time as a resting state. But when they discovered that DNA replication and chromosome duplication occur during interphase, the **cell cycle** concept was proposed. Investigators have also discovered that cytoplasmic organelle duplication occurs during interphase, as does synthesis of the proteins involved in regulating cell division. Thus, the cell cycle can be broken down into four stages (Fig. 8.1). State the event of each stage on the line provided:

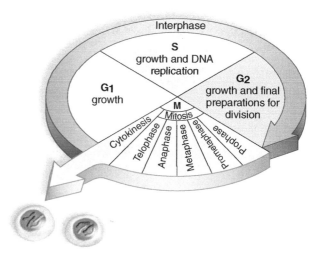

Figure 8.1   The cell cycle.
Immature cells go through a cycle that consists of four stages: G_1, S (for synthesis), G_2, and M (for mitosis). Eventually, some daughter cells "break out" of the cell cycle and become specialized cells.

G_1 _____

S _____

G_2 _____

M _____

Explain why the entire process is called the "cell cycle."

The time required for the entire cell cycle varies according to the organism, but 18 to 24 hours is typical for animal cells. Mitosis (including cytokinesis, if it occurs) lasts less than an hour to slightly more than 2 hours; for the rest of the time, the cell is in interphase.

Table 8.1   Structures Associated with Mitosis

Structure	Description
Nucleus	A large organelle containing the chromosomes and acting as a control center for the cells
Chromosome	Rod-shaped body in the nucleus that is seen during mitosis and meiosis and that contains DNA and, therefore the hereditary units, or genes
Nucleolus	An organelle found inside the nucleus; composed largely of RNA for ribosome formation
Spindle	Microtubule structure that brings about chromosome movement during cell division
Chromatids	The two identical parts of a chromosome following DNA replication
Centromere	A constriction where duplicates (sister chromatids) of a chromosome are held together
Centrosome	The central microtubule-organizing center of cells; consists of granular material; in animal cells, contains two centrioles
Centrioles*	Short, cylindrical organelles in animal cells that contains microtubules and are associated with the formation of the spindle during cell division
Aster*	Short, radiating fibers produced by the centrioles

*Animal cells only

Mitosis

Mitosis is nuclear division that results in two new nuclei, each having the same number of chromosomes as the original nucleus. The **parent cell** is the cell that divides, and the resulting cells are called **daughter cells.**

When cell division is about to begin, chromatin starts to condense and compact to form visible, rodlike sister chromatids held together at the centromere (Fig. 8.2a). *Label the sister chromatids, centromere, and kinetochore in the drawing of a duplicated chromosome in Figure 8.2b.* This illustration represents a chromosome as it would appear just before nuclear division occurs.

Figure 8.2 Duplicated chromosomes.
DNA replication results in a duplicated chromosome that consists of two sister chromatids held together at a centromere. **a.** Scanning electron micrograph of a duplicated chromosome. **b.** Drawing of a duplicated chromosome.

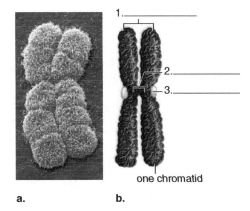

1._____

2._____

3._____

one chromatid

a.   b.

Spindle

Table 8.1 lists the structures that play a role during mitosis. The **spindle** is a structure that appears and brings about an orderly distribution of chromosomes to the daughter cell nuclei. A spindle has fibers that stretch between two poles (ends). Spindle fibers are bundles of microtubules, protein cylinders found in the cytoplasm that can assemble and disassemble. The **centrosome,** the main microtubule-organizing center of the cell, divides before mitosis so that during mitosis, each pole of the spindle has a centrosome. Animal cells contain two barrel-shaped organelles called **centrioles** in each centrosome and asters, arrays of short microtubules radiating from the poles (see Fig. 8.3). The fact that plant cells lack centrioles suggests that centrioles are not required for spindle formation.

Observation: Animal Mitosis

Animal Mitosis Models

1. Using Figure 8.3 as a guide, identify the phases of animal cell mitosis in models of animal cell mitosis.
2. Each species has its own chromosome number. Counting the number of centromeres tells you the number of chromosomes in the models. What is the number of chromosomes in each of the cells

   in this model series? _____

Whitefish Blastula Slide

The blastula is an early embryonic stage in the development of animals. The **blastomeres** (blastula cells) shown are in different phases of mitosis (see Fig. 8.3).

1. Examine a prepared slide of whitefish blastula cells undergoing mitotic cell division.
2. Try to find a cell in each phase of mitosis. Have a partner or your instructor check your identification.

Mitosis Phases

Figure 8.3 Phases of mitosis in animal and plant cells.
The colors signify that the chromosomes were inherited from different parents.

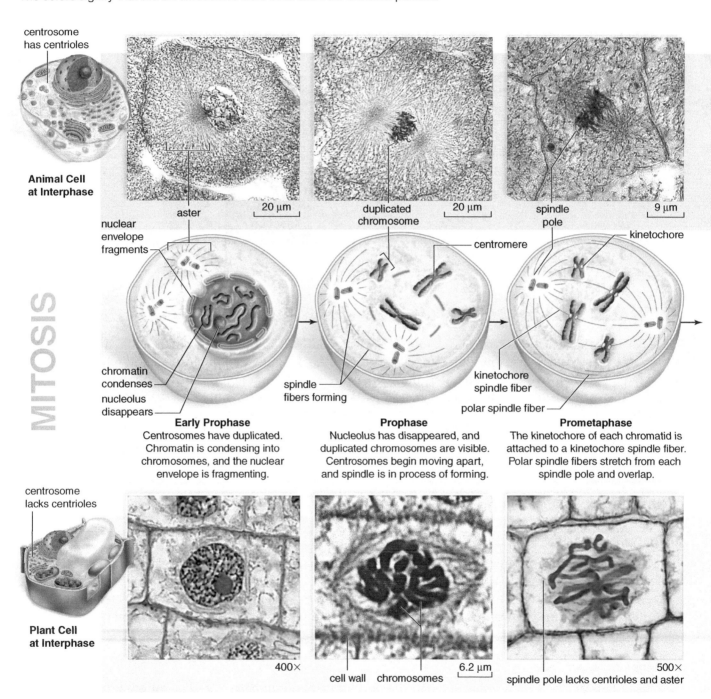

centrosome has centrioles

Animal Cell at Interphase

aster   20 µm

duplicated chromosome   20 µm

spindle pole   9 µm

MITOSIS

nuclear envelope fragments

chromatin condenses

nucleolus disappears

kinetochore

centromere

spindle fibers forming

kinetochore spindle fiber

polar spindle fiber

Early Prophase
Centrosomes have duplicated. Chromatin is condensing into chromosomes, and the nuclear envelope is fragmenting.

Prophase
Nucleolus has disappeared, and duplicated chromosomes are visible. Centrosomes begin moving apart, and spindle is in process of forming.

Prometaphase
The kinetochore of each chromatid is attached to a kinetochore spindle fiber. Polar spindle fibers stretch from each spindle pole and overlap.

centrosome lacks centrioles

Plant Cell at Interphase

400×

cell wall   chromosomes   6.2 µm

500×
spindle pole lacks centrioles and aster

The phases of mitosis are shown in Figure 8.3. Mitosis is the type of nuclear division that (1) occurs in the body (somatic) cells; (2) results in two daughter cells because there is only one round of division; and (3) keeps the chromosome number constant (same as the parent cell).

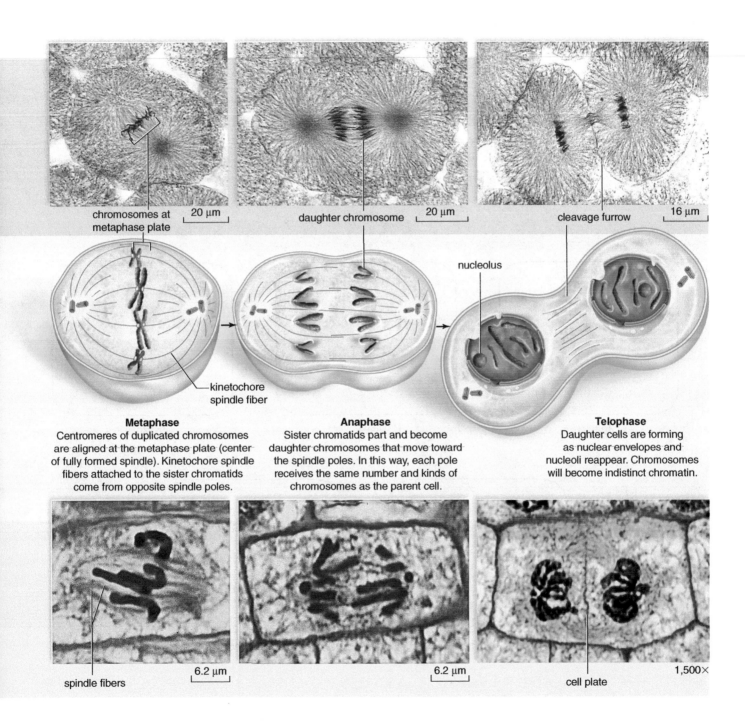

chromosomes at metaphase plate · 20 μm

daughter chromosome · 20 μm

cleavage furrow · 16 μm

nucleolus

kinetochore spindle fiber

Metaphase
Centromeres of duplicated chromosomes are aligned at the metaphase plate (center of fully formed spindle). Kinetochore spindle fibers attached to the sister chromatids come from opposite spindle poles.

Anaphase
Sister chromatids part and become daughter chromosomes that move toward the spindle poles. In this way, each pole receives the same number and kinds of chromosomes as the parent cell.

Telophase
Daughter cells are forming as nuclear envelopes and nucleoli reappear. Chromosomes will become indistinct chromatin.

spindle fibers · 6.2 μm

6.2 μm

cell plate · 1,500×

Observation: Plant Mitosis

Plant Mitosis Models

1. Identify the phases of plant cell mitosis using models of plant cell mitosis and Figure 8.3 as a guide.
2. Notice that plant cells do not have centrioles and asters. Plant cells do have centrosomes and this accounts for the formation of a spindle.
3. What is the number of chromosomes in each of the cells in this model series? _____

Onion Root Tip Slide

1. In plants, the root tip contains tissue that is continually dividing and producing new cells. Examine a prepared slide of onion root tip cells undergoing mitotic cell division. Try to find the phases that correspond to those shown in Figure 8.3.
2. Using high power, focus up and down on a cell in telophase. You may be able to just make out the cell plate, the region where a plasma membrane is forming between the two prospective daughter cells. Later, cell walls appear in this area.
3. In the boxes provided, draw and label the stages of mitosis as observed in the onion root tip slide.

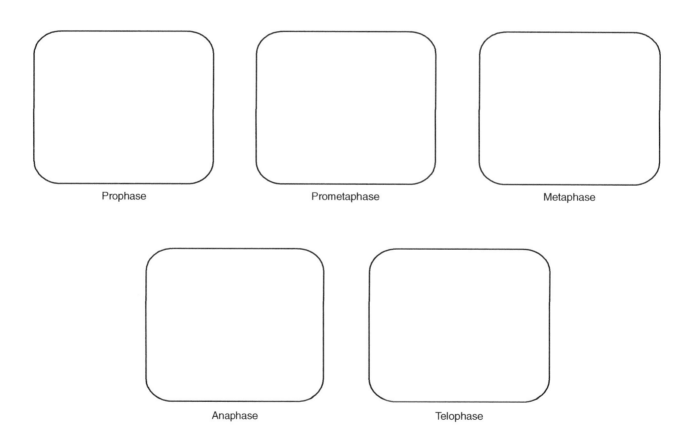

Prophase   Prometaphase   Metaphase

Anaphase   Telophase

Cytokinesis

Cytokinesis, division of the cytoplasm, usually accompanies mitosis. During cytokinesis, each daughter cell receives a share of the organelles that duplicated during interphase. Cytokinesis begins in anaphase, continues in telophase, and reaches completion by the start of the next interphase.

Cytokinesis in Animal Cells

In animal cells, a **cleavage furrow,** an indentation of the membrane between the daughter nuclei, begins as anaphase draws to a close (Fig. 8.4). The cleavage furrow deepens as a band of actin filaments called the contractile ring slowly constricts the cell, forming two daughter cells.

Were any of the cells of the whitefish blastula slide undergoing cytokinesis? _____

How do you know? _____

_____

_____

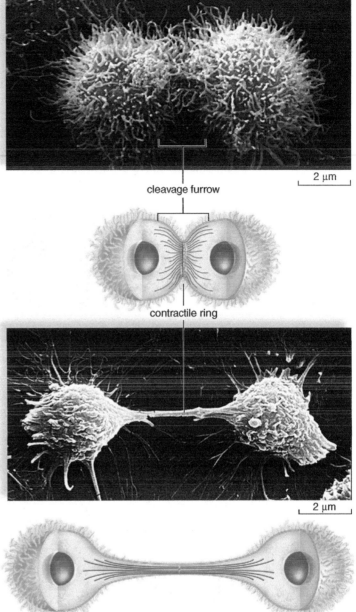

cleavage furrow

contractile ring

2 μm

2 μm

Figure 8.4   Cytokinesis in animal cells.
A single cell becomes two cells by a furrowing process. A contractile ring composed of actin filaments gradually gets smaller, and the cleavage furrow pinches the cell into two cells.
Copyright by R. G. Kessel and C. Y. Shih, *Scanning Electron Microscopy in Biology: A Students' Atlas on Biological Organization,* Springer-Verlag, 1974.

Cytokinesis in Plant Cells

After mitosis, the cytoplasm divides by cytokinesis. In plant cells, membrane vesicles derived from the Golgi apparatus migrate to the center of the cell and form a **cell plate** (Fig. 8.5), the location of a new plasma membrane for each daughter cell. Later, individual cell walls appear in this area. Were any of the cells of the onion root tip slide undergoing cytokinesis? _____

How do you know? _____

Figure 8.5   Cytokinesis in plant cells.
During cytokinesis in a plant cell, a cell plate forms midway between two daughter nuclei and extends to the plasma membrane. Vesicles containing cell wall components fuse to form cell plate.

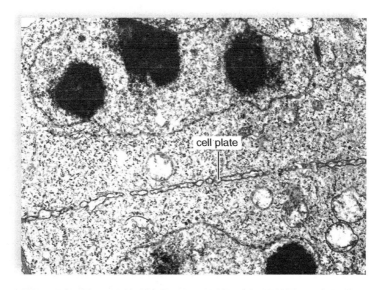

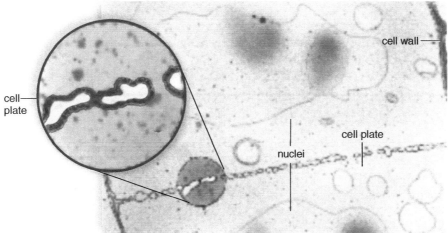

Summary of Mitotic Cell Division

1. The nuclei in the daughter cells have the _____ number of chromosomes as the parent cell had.

2. Mitosis is cell division in which the chromosome number _____

3. Answer this question. If a parent cell has 16 chromosomes, how many chromosomes do the daughter cells have following mitosis? _____

8.2 Meiosis

Meiosis is a form of nuclear division in which the chromosome number is reduced by half. The nucleus of the parent cell has the diploid (2n) number of chromosomes—that is, two sets of chromosomes. After meiosis is complete, the daughter nuclei have the haploid (n) number, or one set of chromosomes. For example, diploid fruit fly cells have 8 chromosomes (2n = 8) but undergo meiosis to produce gametes with 4 chromosomes (n = 4). In sexually reproducing species, meiosis must occur or the chromosome number would double with each generation.

A diploid nucleus contains **homologues,** also called homologous chromosomes. Homologues look alike and carry the genes for the same traits. Before meiosis begins, the chromosomes are already double stranded—that is, they contain sister chromatids.

Experimental Procedure: Meiosis

In this exercise, you will use pop beads to construct homologues and move the chromosomes to simulate meiosis.

Building Chromosomes to Simulate Meiosis

1. Obtain the following materials: 48 pop beads of one color (e.g., red) and 48 pop beads of another color (e.g., blue) for a total of 96 beads; eight magnetic centromeres; and four centriole groups.
2. Build a homologous pair of duplicated chromosomes using Figure 8.6*a* as a guide. Each chromatid will have 16 beads. Be sure to bring the centromeres of two units of the same color together so that they attract and link to form one duplicated chromosome. (One member of the pair will be red, and the other will be blue.)
3. Build another homologous pair of duplicated chromosomes using Figure 8.6*b* as a guide. Each chromatid will have eight beads. Be sure to bring the centromeres of two units of the same color together so that they attract. (One member of the pair will be red, and the other will be blue.)
4. Note that your chromosomes are the same as those in Figure 8.7. The red chromosomes were inherited from one parent, and the blue chromosomes were inherited from the other parent.

Figure 8.6 Two pairs of homologues.
The chromosomes of these homologous pairs are duplicated.

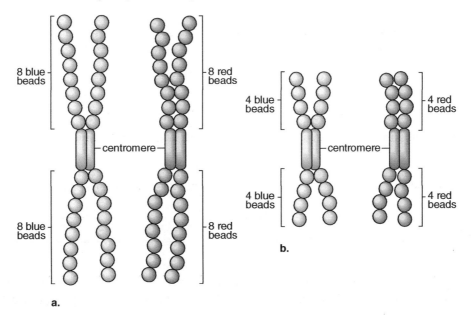

Meiosis I

Meiosis requires two nuclear divisions, and the first round during meiosis is called **meiosis I** (see Fig. 8.7).

During prophase of meiosis I, the spindle appears while the nuclear envelope and nucleolus disappear. Homologues line up next to one another during a process called **synapsis.** During **crossing-over,** the nonsister chromatids of a homologue pair exchange genetic material. At metaphase I, the homologue pairs line up at the metaphase plate of the spindle. During anaphase I, homologues separate and the chromosomes (still composed of two chromatids) move to each pole. In telophase I, the nuclear envelope and the nucleolus reappear as the spindle disappears. Each new nucleus contains one from each pair of chromosomes.

Prophase I

5. Using Figure 8.7 as a guide, put all four of the chromosomes you built in the center of your work area, which represents the nucleus. Place two pairs of centrioles outside the nucleus.
6. Separate the pairs of centrioles, and move one pair to opposite poles of the nucleus.
7. Synapsis is the pairing of homologues during prophase I. Simulate synapsis by bringing the homologues together.
8. **Crossing-over** is an exchange of genetic material between two homologues. It is a way to achieve genetic recombination during meiosis. Simulate crossing-over by exchanging the exact segments of two nonsister chromatids of a single homologous pair. Why use nonsister chromatids and not sister

   chromatids? _____

Metaphase I

Position the homologues at the metaphase plate in such a way that the homologues are prepared to move apart toward the centrioles.

Anaphase I

Separate the homologues, and move each one toward the opposite pole.

Telophase I

9. During telophase I, the chromosomes are at the poles. What combinations of chromosomes are at the poles? Fill in the following blanks with the words *red-long, red-short, blue-long,* and *blue-short:*

   Pole A: _____ and _____

   Pole B: _____ and _____

10. What other combinations would have been possible? (*Hint:* Alternate the colors at metaphase I.)

   Pole A: _____ and _____

   Pole B: _____ and _____

Conclusions: Meiosis I

- Do the chromosomes inherited from the mother or father have to remain together following

  meiosis I? _____

- Name two ways that meiosis contributes to genetic variation among offspring:

  a. _____

  b. _____

Interkinesis

Interkinesis is the period between meiosis I and meiosis II. In some species, daughter cells do not form, and meiosis II follows right after meiosis I. Does DNA replication occur during interkinesis? _____

Explain. _____

Meiosis II

The second round of nuclear division during meiosis is called **meiosis II** (see Fig. 8.7).

During prophase of meiosis II, a spindle appears. Each chromosome attaches to the spindle individually. During metaphase II, the chromosomes are lined up at the metaphase plate. During anaphase II, the centromeres divide and the chromatids separate, becoming daughter chromosomes that move toward the poles. In telophase II, the spindle disappears as the nuclear envelope reappears. Notice that meiosis II is exactly like mitosis except that the nucleus of the parent cell and the daughter nuclei are haploid.

Prophase II

1. Using Figure 8.7 as a guide, choose the chromosomes from one telophase I pole (see step 9, page 92) to represent those in the parent nucleus undergoing meiosis II.
2. Place two pairs of centrioles at opposite sides of these chromosomes to form the new spindle.

Metaphase II

Move the duplicated chromosomes to the metaphase plate. How many chromosomes are at the

metaphase plate? _____

Anaphase II

Pull the two magnets of each duplicated chromosome apart. What does this action represent? _____

_____

Telophase II

Put the chromosomes—each having one chromatid—at the poles near the centrioles.

Conclusions: Meiosis II

- You chose only one daughter nucleus from meiosis I to be the nucleus that divides. In reality both daughter nuclei go on to divide again. Therefore, how many nuclei are usually present when

  meiosis II is complete? _____

- In this exercise, how many chromosomes were in the parent cell nucleus undergoing meiosis II?

  _____

- How many chromosomes are in the daughter nuclei? _____ Explain.

_____

_____

Summary of Meiotic Cell Division

1. The parent cell has the diploid (2n) number of chromosomes, and the daughter cells have the _____ (n) number of chromosomes.
2. Meiosis is cell division in which the chromosome number _____
3. If a parent cell has 16 chromosomes, the daughter cells will have how many chromosomes following meiosis? _____
4. Whereas meiosis reduces the chromosome number, **fertilization** restores the chromosome number. A zygote contains the same number of chromosomes as the parent, but are these exactly the same chromosomes as either parent had? _____
5. What is another way that sexual reproduction results in genetic variation?

_____

Meiosis Phases

Figure 8.7   Meiosis I and II in plant cell micrographs and animal cell drawings. Crossing-over occurred during meiosis I.

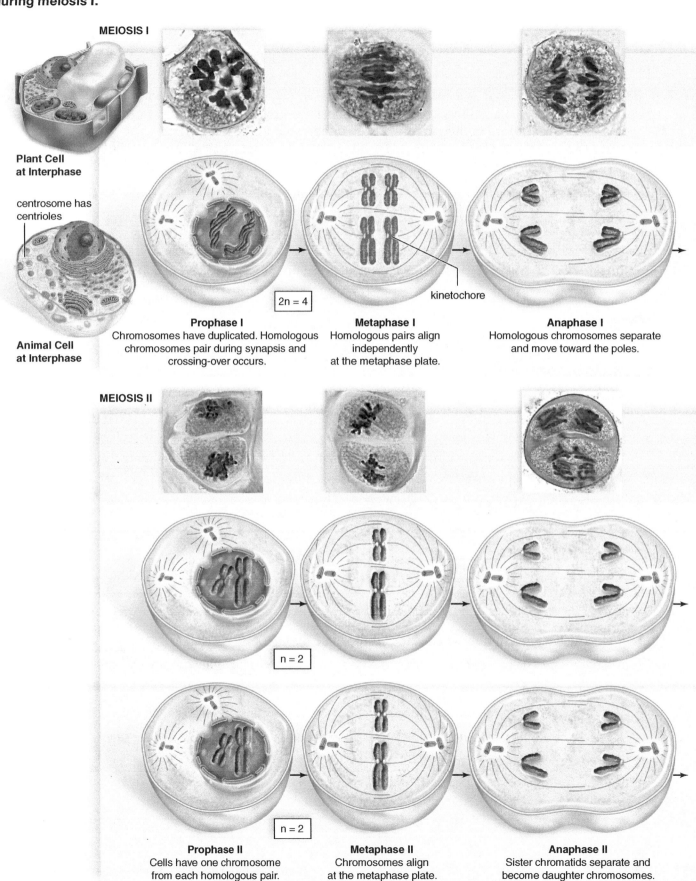

MEIOSIS I

Plant Cell at Interphase

centrosome has centrioles

Animal Cell at Interphase

2n = 4

kinetochore

Prophase I
Chromosomes have duplicated. Homologous chromosomes pair during synapsis and crossing-over occurs.

Metaphase I
Homologous pairs align independently at the metaphase plate.

Anaphase I
Homologous chromosomes separate and move toward the poles.

MEIOSIS II

n = 2

n = 2

Prophase II
Cells have one chromosome from each homologous pair.

Metaphase II
Chromosomes align at the metaphase plate.

Anaphase II
Sister chromatids separate and become daughter chromosomes.

The phases of meiosis are shown in Figure 8.7. Meiosis is the type of nuclear division that (1) occurs in the sex organs (testes and ovaries); (2) results in four cells because there are two rounds of cell division; and (3) reduces the chromosome number to half that of the parent cell.

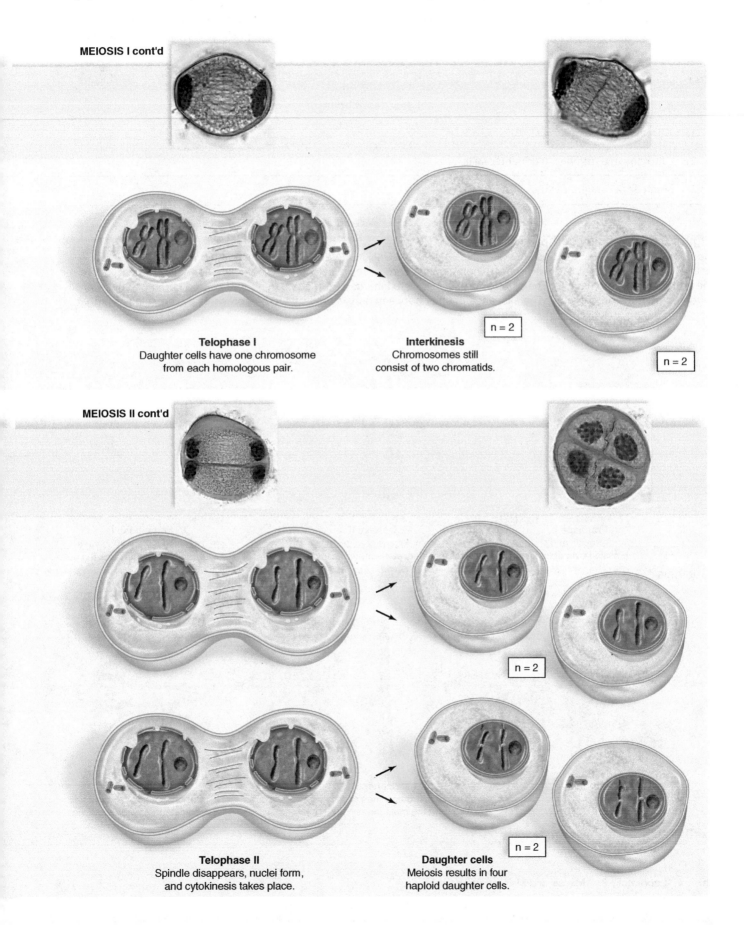

MEIOSIS I cont'd

Telophase I
Daughter cells have one chromosome
from each homologous pair.

Interkinesis
Chromosomes still
consist of two chromatids.

n = 2

n = 2

MEIOSIS II cont'd

Telophase II
Spindle disappears, nuclei form,
and cytokinesis takes place.

Daughter cells
Meiosis results in four
haploid daughter cells.

n = 2

n = 2

8.3 Mitosis Versus Meiosis

In comparing mitosis to meiosis it is important to note that meiosis requires two nuclear divisions but mitosis requires only one nuclear division. Therefore mitosis produces two daughter cells and meiosis produces four daughter cells. Following mitosis, the daughter cells are still diploid but following meiosis, the daughter cells are haploid. Figure 8.8 explains why. Fill in Table 8.2 to indicate general

Table 8.2 Differences Between Mitosis and Meiosis	Mitosis	Meiosis
1. Number of divisions		
2. Chromosome number in daughter cells		
3. Number of daughter cells		

Figure 8.8 Meiosis I compared to mitosis.

Compare metaphase I of meiosis I to metaphase of mitosis. Only in metaphase I are the homologous chromosomes paired at the metaphase plate. Members of homologous chromosome pairs separate during anaphase I, and therefore the daughter cells are haploid. The blue chromosomes were inherited from one parent, and the red chromosomes were inherited from the other parent. The exchange of color between nonsister chromatids represents the crossing-over that occurred during meiosis I.

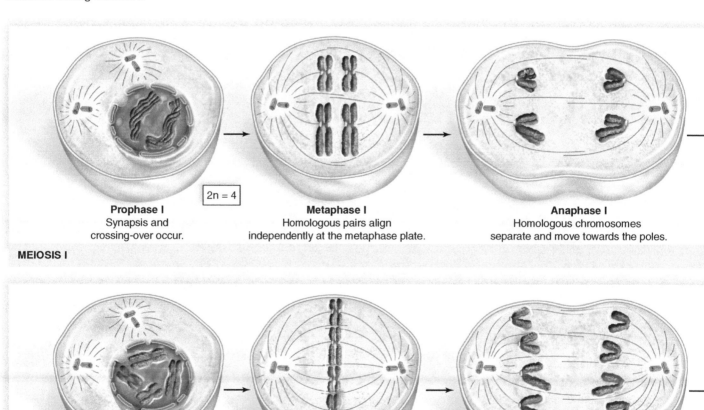

Prophase I
Synapsis and
crossing-over occur.

2n = 4

Metaphase I
Homologous pairs align
independently at the metaphase plate.

Anaphase I
Homologous chromosomes
separate and move towards the poles.

MEIOSIS I

Prophase

2n = 4

Metaphase
Chromosomes align
at the metaphase plate.

Anaphase
Sister chromatids separate and
become daughter chromosomes.

MITOSIS

differences between mitosis and meiosis and complete Table 8.3 to indicate specific differences between mitosis and meiosis I. Mitosis need only be compared with meiosis I because the exact events occur during both mitosis and meiosis II except that the cells are diploid during mitosis and haploid during meiosis II.

Table 8.3   Mitosis Compared with Meiosis I

Mitosis	Meiosis I
Prophase: No pairing of chromosomes	Prophase I: _____
Metaphase: Duplicated chromosomes at metaphase plate	Metaphase I: _____
Anaphase: Sister chromatids separate	Anaphase I: _____
Telophase: Chromosomes have one chromatid	Telophase I: _____

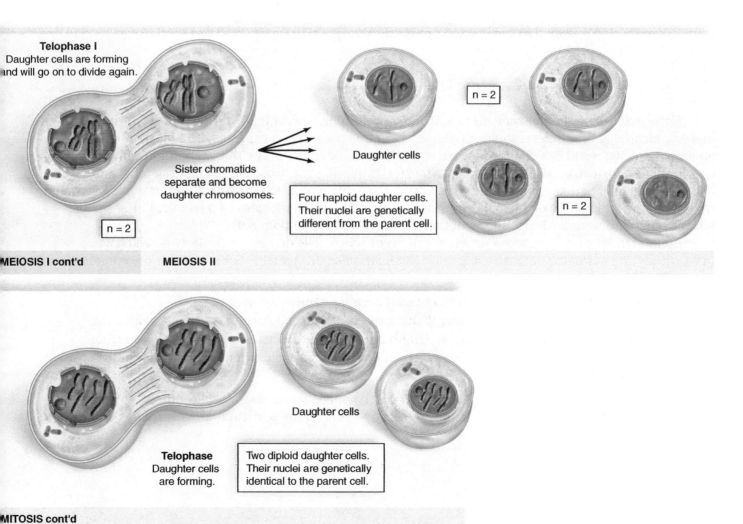

Telophase I
Daughter cells are forming and will go on to divide again.

n = 2

Sister chromatids separate and become daughter chromosomes.

Daughter cells

n = 2

Four haploid daughter cells. Their nuclei are genetically different from the parent cell.

n = 2

n = 2

MEIOSIS I cont'd   MEIOSIS II

Telophase
Daughter cells are forming.

Daughter cells

Two diploid daughter cells. Their nuclei are genetically identical to the parent cell.

MITOSIS cont'd

8.4   Karyotype Abnormalities

In a karyotype, the chromosomes of an organism are arranged so that the pairs of chromosomes can be seen (Fig. 8.9). At that time, it is possible to observe any possible abnormalities in chromosome number and structure.

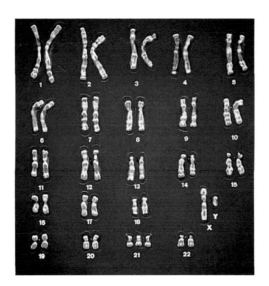

Figure 8.9   Karyotype of a person with Down syndrome.
Note the three number 21 chromosomes.

Abnormalities of chromosome number usually occur when cells divide during mitosis or during meiosis, signifying that these complex processes don't always occur as expected. The most common abnormal meiotic result is a change in number so that the individual has either 45 chromosomes or 47 chromosomes, instead of 46 chromosomes. An extra or missing chromosome can cause a fetus and/or a child to develop apparent abnormalities. For example, a fetus who has a missing X chromosome may fail to develop the appearance of a female and may not have the internal organs of a female. Either sex that has an extra chromosome 21 has the symptoms of Down syndrome (Fig. 8.9).

Abnormalities of chromosome structure can occur when cells divide, particularly if cells have been subject to environmental influences such as radiation or drug intake. Some of the more common structural abnormalities are:

Deletion: The chromosome is shorter than usual because some portion is missing.
Duplication: The chromosome is longer than usual because some portion is present twice over.
Inversion: The chromosome is normal in length but some portion runs in the opposite direction.
Translocation: Two chromosomes have switched portions and each switched portion is on the wrong chromosome.

Abnormalities of chromosome structure can result in recognized syndromes, a collection of symptoms that always occur together. Which syndrome appears depends on the particular abnormality.

8.5 Gametogenesis in Animals

Gametogenesis is the formation of **gametes** (sex cells) in animals. In humans and other mammals, the gametes are sperm and eggs. **Fertilization** occurs when the nucleus of a sperm fuses with the nucleus of an egg.

Gametogenesis in Mammals

Gametogenesis occurs in the testes of males, where **spermatogenesis** produces sperm. Gametogenesis occurs in the ovaries of females, where **oogenesis** produces oocytes (eggs).

A **diploid** (2n) nucleus contains the full number of chromosomes, which is 46 in humans, and a **haploid** (n) nucleus contains half as many, which is 23 in humans. Gametogenesis involves **meiosis,** the process that reduces the chromosome number from 2n to n. In sexually reproducing species, if meiosis did not occur, the chromosome number would double with each generation. Meiosis consists of two divisions: the first meiotic division (meiosis I) and the second meiotic division (meiosis II). Therefore, you would expect four haploid cells at the end of the process. Indeed, there are four sperm as a result of spermatogenesis (Fig. 8.10). However, in females, meiosis I results in a secondary oocyte and one polar body. A **polar body** is a nonfunctioning cell that will disintegrate. A secondary oocyte does not undergo meiosis II unless fertilization (fusion of egg and sperm) occurs. At the completion of oogenesis, there is a single egg and at least two polar bodies (Fig. 8.10).

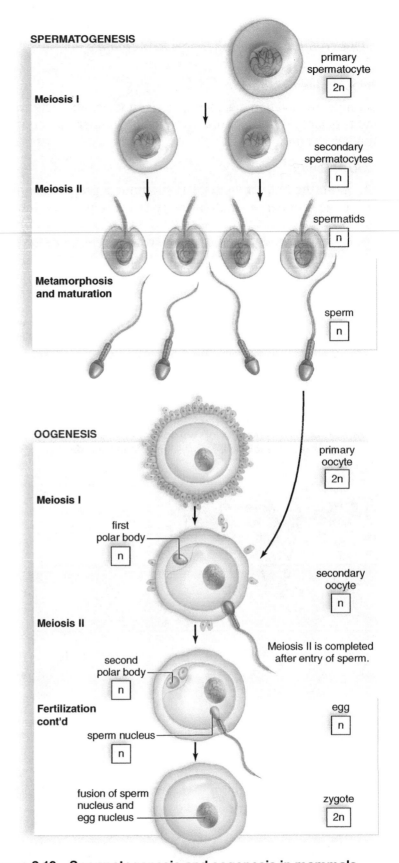

Figure 8.10 Spermatogenesis and oogenesis in mammals.
Spermatogenesis produces four viable sperm, whereas oogenesis produces one egg and two polar bodies. In humans, both sperm and egg have 23 chromosomes each; therefore, following fertilization, the zygote has 46 chromosomes.

Observation: Gametogenesis in Mammals

Gametogenesis Models

Examine any available gametogenesis models, and determine the diploid number of the parent cell and the haploid number of a gamete. Remember that counting the number of centromeres tells you the number of chromosomes.

Slide of Ovary

1. With the help of Figure 8.11, examine a prepared slide of an ovary. Under low power, you will see a large number of small, primary follicles near the outer edge. A primary follicle contains a primary oocyte.
2. Find a secondary follicle, and switch to high power. Note the secondary oocyte (egg), surrounded by numerous cells, to one side of the liquid-filled follicle.
3. Also look for a large, fluid-filled vesicular (Graafian) follicle, which contains a mature secondary oocyte to one side. The vesicular follicle will be next to the outer surface of the ovary because this type of follicle releases the egg during ovulation.
4. How many secondary follicles can you find on your slide? _____ How many vesicular follicles can you find? _____ How does this number compare with the number of sperm cells seen in the testis cross section (see Fig. 8.12)? _____

Figure 8.11 Microscopic ovary anatomy.

The stages of follicle and oocyte (egg) development are shown in sequence. Each follicle goes through all the stages. Following ovulation, a follicle becomes the corpus luteum.

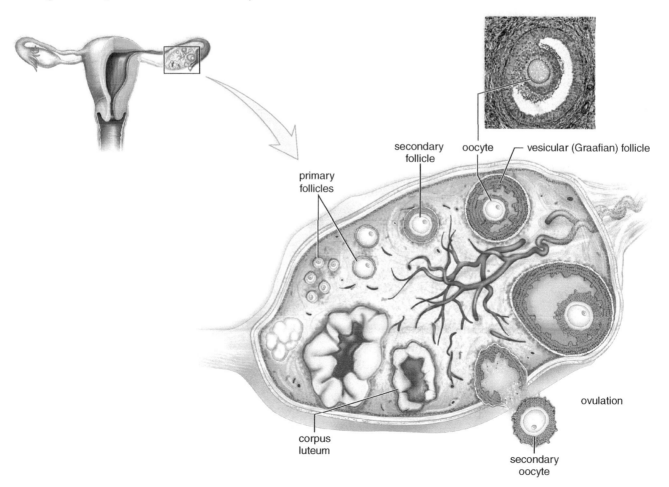

Slide of Testis

1. With the help of Figure 8.12, examine a prepared slide of a testis. Under low power, note the many circular structures. These are the **seminiferous tubules,** where sperm formation takes place.
2. Switch to high power, and observe one tubule in particular. Find mature sperm (which look like thin, fine, dark lines) in the middle of the tubule. **Interstitial cells,** which produce the male sex hormone testosterone, are between the tubules.

Summary of Gametogenesis

1. What is gametogenesis? _____

   In general, how many chromosomes are in a gamete? _____

2. What is spermatogenesis? _____

   How many chromosomes does a human sperm have? _____

3. What is oogenesis? _____

   How many chromosomes does a human egg have? _____

4. Following fertilization, how many chromosomes does the zygote, the first cell of the new

   individual, have? _____

Figure 8.12   Microscopic testis anatomy.

a. A testis contains many seminiferous tubules. **b.** Scanning electron micrograph of a cross section of the seminiferous tubules, where spermatogenesis occurs. Note the location of interstitial cells in clumps among the seminiferous tubules in this light micrograph.

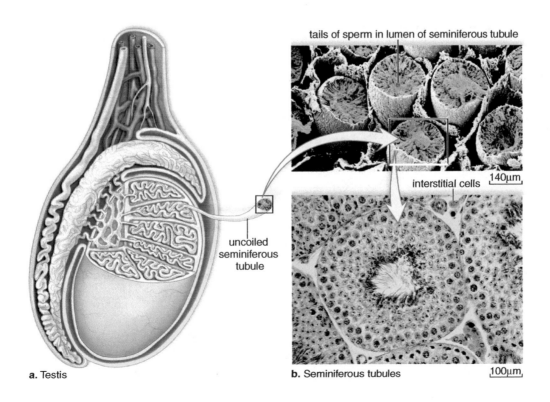

tails of sperm in lumen of seminiferous tubule

interstitial cells   140μm

uncoiled seminiferous tubule

a. Testis

b. Seminiferous tubules   100μm

Laboratory Review 8

1. During anaphase of mitosis in humans or other 2n organisms, do the chromosomes have one or two chromatids as they move toward the poles? _____

2. During anaphase of meiosis I, do the chromosomes have one or two chromatids as they move toward the poles? _____

3. During anaphase of meiosis II, do the chromosomes have one or two chromatids as they move toward the poles? _____

4. Asexual reproduction of a haploid protozoan can be described as n → n. Explain. _____
_____

5. Explain why furrowing is a suitable mechanism for cytokinesis of animal cells but not plant cells.
_____

6. A student is simulating meiosis I with chromosomes that are red-long and yellow-long; red-short and yellow-short. Why would you *not* expect to find both red-long and yellow-long in one resulting daughter cell? _____
_____

7. If there are 13 pairs of homologous chromosomes in a primary spermatocyte, how many chromosomes are there in a sperm? _____

8. Assume that you have built a homologous pair of chromosomes, each having two chromatids. One homologue contains red beads, while the other contains yellow beads.
Describe the appearance of two nonsister chromatids following crossing-over. _____
_____

9. What are the major differences between mitosis and meiosis? _____
_____

10. A person with Down syndrome has what type of chromosome abnormality? _____

Biology Website

The companion website for *Biology* provides a wealth of information organized and integrated by chapter. You will find practice tests, animations, videos, and much more that will complement your learning and understanding of general biology.

www.mhhe.com/maderbiology10

McGraw-Hill Access Science Website

An Encyclopedia of Science and Technology Online which provides more information including videos that can enhance the laboratory experience.

www.accessscience.com

Learning Outcomes

9.1 One-Trait Crosses
- State Mendel's law of segregation, and relate this law to laboratory exercises.   104–10
- Describe the life cycle of *Drosophila* (fruit fly), and recognize these stages in a culture bottle.   106–7
- Describe and predict the results of a one-trait cross in both tobacco seedlings and *Drosophila*.   104–7

9.2 Two-Trait Crosses
- State Mendel's law of independent assortment, and relate this law to laboratory exercises.   110–13
- Explain and predict the results of a two-trait cross in corn plants and *Drosophila*.   111–13

9.3 X-Linked Crosses
- Explain and predict the results of a cross in *Drosophila* for X-linked genes.   114–15

9.4 Chi-Square Analysis
- Utilize the chi-square statistical test to help determine whether data do or do not support a hypothesis.   116–17

Introduction

Gregor Mendel, sometimes called the "father of genetics," formulated the basic laws of genetics examined in this laboratory. He determined that individuals have two alternate forms of a gene (two **alleles**, in modern terminology) for each trait in their body cells. Today, we know that alleles are on the chromosomes. An individual can be homozygous dominant (two dominant alleles, *GG*), homozygous recessive (two recessive alleles, *gg*), or heterozygous (one dominant and one recessive allele, *Gg*). **Genotype** refers to an individual's genes, while **phenotype** refers to an individual's appearance (Fig. 9.1). Homozygous dominant and heterozygous individuals show the dominant phenotype; homozygous recessive individuals show the recessive phenotype.

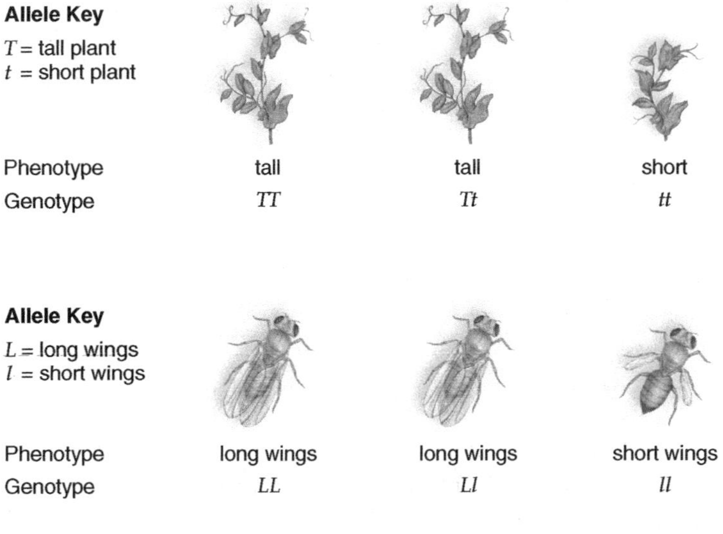

Figure 9.1   Genotype versus phenotype.
Only with homozygous recessive do you immediately know the genotype.

Allele Key
T = tall plant
t = short plant

Phenotype	tall	tall	short
Genotype	*TT*	*Tt*	*tt*

Allele Key
L = long wings
l = short wings

Phenotype	long wings	long wings	short wings
Genotype	*LL*	*Ll*	*ll*

9.1 One-Trait Crosses

A single pair of alleles is involved in one-trait crosses. Mendel found that reproduction between two heterozygous individuals *(Aa)*, called a monohybrid cross, resulted in both dominant and recessive phenotypes among the offspring. The expected phenotypic ratio among the offspring was 3:1. Three offspring had the dominant phenotype for every one that had the recessive phenotype.

Mendel realized that these results were obtainable only if the alleles of each parent segregated (separated from each other) during meiosis (otherwise, all offspring would inherit a dominant allele, and no offspring would be homozygous recessive). Therefore, Mendel formulated his first law of inheritance:

Law of Segregation

Each organism contains two alleles for each trait, and the alleles segregate during the formation of gametes. Each gamete then contains only one allele for each trait. When fertilization occurs, the new organism has two alleles for each trait, one from each parent.

Inheritance is a game of chance. Just as there is a 50% probability of heads or tails when tossing a coin, there is a 50% probability that a sperm or egg will have an A or an a when the parent is Aa. The chance of an equal number of heads or tails improves as the number of tosses increases. In the same way, the chance of an equal number of gametes with A and a improves as the number of gametes increases. Therefore, the 3:1 ratio among offspring is more likely when a large number of sperm fertilize a large number of eggs.

Color of Tobacco Seedlings

In tobacco plants, a dominant allele *(C)* for chlorophyll gives the plants a green color, and a recessive allele *(c)* for chlorophyll causes a plant to appear white. If a tobacco plant is homozygous for the recessive allele *(c)*, it cannot manufacture chlorophyll and thus appears white (Fig. 9.2).

Figure 9.2 Monohybrid cross.
These tobacco seedlings are growing on an agar plate. The white plants cannot manufacture chlorophyll.

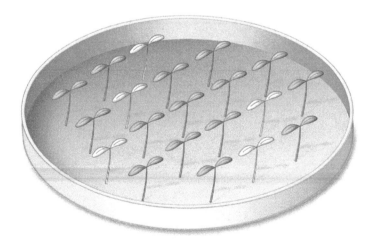

Experimental Procedure: Color of Tobacco Seedlings

1. Obtain a numbered agar plate on which tobacco seedlings are growing. They are the offspring of the cross $Cc \times Cc$. Complete the Punnett square.

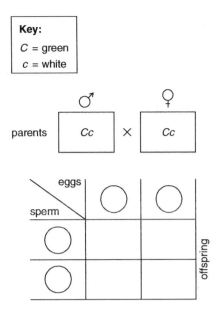

Key:
C = green
c = white

parents Cc × Cc
           ♂   ♀

eggs

sperm

offspring

What is the expected phenotypic ratio? _____

2. Using a stereomicroscope, view the seedlings, and count the number that are green and the number that are white. Record the plate number and your results in Table 9.1.

3. Repeat steps 1 and 2 for two additional plates. Total the number that are green and the number that are white.

4. Complete Table 9.1 by recording the class data.

Table 9.1 Color of Tobacco Seedlings		
	Number of Offspring	
	Green Color	White Color
Plate # _____		
Plate # _____		
Plate # _____		
Totals		
Class data		

Conclusions: Color of Tobacco Seedlings

- Calculate the actual phenotypic ratio you observed. _____ Do your results differ from the expected ratio? _____ Explain. _____

  _____

- Do a chi-square test (see Section 9.4 of this laboratory) to determine if the deviation from the expected results can be accounted for by chance alone. Chi-square value: _____

- Repeat these steps using the class data. Do your class data give a ratio that is closer to the expected ratio, and is the chi-square deviation insignificant? _____ Explain. _____

  _____

Drosophila Melanogaster Characteristics

Both the adults and the larvae of *Drosophila melanogaster* (the fruit fly) feed on plant sugars and on the wild yeasts that grow on rotting fruit. The female flies first lay **eggs** on these same materials. After a day or two, the eggs hatch into small **larvae** that feed and grow for about eight days, depending on the temperature. During this period, they **molt** twice. Therefore, three larval periods of growth, called **instars**, occur between molts. When fully grown, the third-stage instar larvae cease feeding and **pupate**. During pupation, which lasts about four days, the larval tissues are reorganized to form those of the adult. The life cycle is summarized in Figure 9.3.

Figure 9.3   Life cycle of the fruit fly, showing differences between adult sexes.

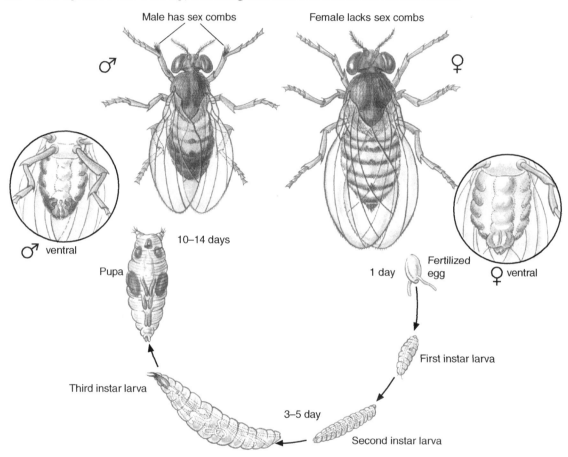

Observation: Drosophila melanogaster

Culture

You will be provided with a stock culture of *Drosophila melanogaster* to examine. Answer the following questions:

1. Where in the culture vial are the adult flies? _____

2. The eggs? _____

3. The larvae? _____

4. The pupae? _____

Flies

You will be provided with either slides, frozen flies, or live flies to examine. If the flies are alive, follow the directions on page 108 for using FlyNap™ to anesthetize them.

1. Put frozen or anesthetized flies on a white card, and use a camel-hair brush to move them around. Use a stereomicroscope or a hand lens to see the flies clearly.
2. If you are looking at slides, you may use the scanning lens of your compound light microscope to view the flies.
3. Examine wild-type flies. Complete Table 9.2 for wild-type flies. Long wings extend beyond the body, and short (vestigial) wings do not extend beyond the body.
4. Examine mutant flies. Complete Table 9.2 for all the mutant flies you examined.

Table 9.2 Characteristics of Wild-Type and Mutant Flies

	Wild-Type	Ebony Body	Short-Wing	Sepia-Eye	White-Eye
Wing length					
Color of eyes					
Color of body					

5. Use the following characteristics to distinguish male flies from female flies (Fig. 9.3):
   - The male is generally smaller.
   - The male has a more rounded abdomen than the female. The female has a pointed abdomen.
   - Dorsally, the male is seen to have a black-tipped abdomen, whereas the female appears to have dark lines only at the tip.
   - Ventrally, the abdomen of the male has a dark region at the tip due to the presence of claspers; this dark region is lacking in the female.

6. In animals such as fruit flies, chromosomes differ between the sexes (Fig. 9.4). All but one pair of chromosomes in males and females are the same; these are called **autosomes** because they do not actively determine sex. The pair that is different is called the **sex chromosomes**. In fruit flies and humans, the sex chromosomes in females are XX and those in males are XY. Some genes on the X chromosome have nothing to do with gender and these genes are said to be X-linked. The Y chromosome does not carry these genes and indeed carries very few genes.

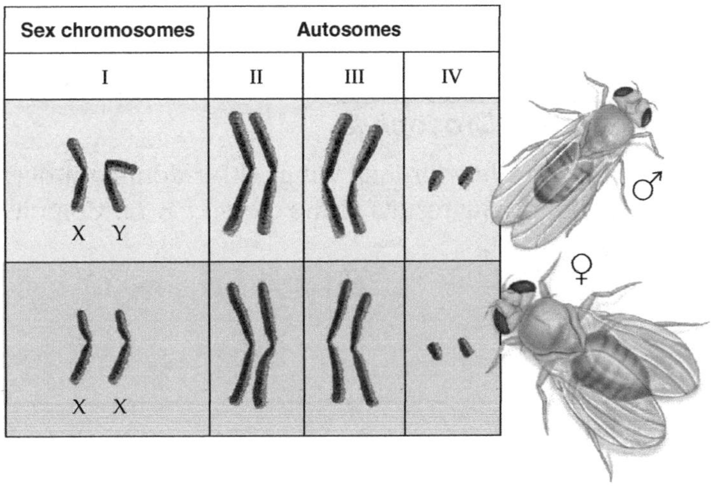

Figure 9.4 *Drosophila* chromosomes.
In *Drosophila* (fruit flies), both males and females have eight chromosomes: three pairs of autosomes (II–IV), and one pair of sex chromosomes (I). Males are XY, and females are XX.

Anesthetizing Flies

The use of FlyNap™ allows flies to be anesthetized for at least 50 minutes without killing them.

1. Dip the absorbent end of a swab into the FlyNap™ bottle, as shown in Figure 9.5.
2. Tap the bottom of the culture vial on the tabletop to knock the flies to the bottom of the vial. (If the medium is not firm, you may wish to transfer the flies to an empty bottle before anesthetizing them. Ask your instructor for assistance, if this is the case.)
3. With one finger, push the plug slightly to one side. Remove the swab from the FlyNap™, and quickly stick the anesthetic end into the culture vial beside the plug so that the anesthetic tip is below the plug. Keep the culture vial upright with the swab in one place.
4. Remove the plug and the swab immediately after the flies are anesthetized (approximately 2 minutes in an empty vial, 4 minutes in a vial with medium), and spill the flies out onto a white file card. The length of time the flies remain anesthetized depends on the amount of FlyNap™ on the swab and on the number and age of the flies in the culture vial.
5. Transfer the anesthetized flies from the white file card onto the glass plate of a stereomicroscope for examination, or use a hand lens.

Figure 9.5 FlyNap™.
Flies can be anesthetized for at least 50 minutes without being killed in FlyNap™.

a. Moisten swab in FlyNap™.

b. Insert swab into culture bottle.

c. Remove flies as shown.

Wing Length in *Drosophila*

In fruit flies, the allele for long wings (*L*) is dominant over the allele for short (vestigial) wings (*l*). You will be examining the results of the cross *Ll* × *Ll*. Complete this Punnett square:

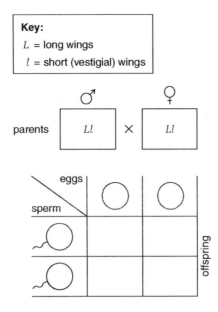

Key:
L = long wings
l = short (vestigial) wings

parents Ll × Ll

eggs

sperm

offspring

What is the expected phenotypic ratio among the offspring? _____

Experimental Procedure: Wing Length in Drosophila

The cross described here will take three weeks. The experiment can be done in one week, however, if your instructor provides you with a vial that already contains the results of the cross $Ll \times Ll$. In this case, proceed directly to week 3. Alternately your instructor may provide you with data. In that case, enter the data into Table 9.3 and proceed directly to the Conclusions on page 110.

1. **Week 1:** Place heterozygous flies in a prepared culture vial. Your instructor will show you how to use instant medium and dry yeast to prepare the vial. Label your culture. What is the phenotype of

   heterozygous flies? _____

   What is the genotype of heterozygous flies? _____

2. **Week 2:** Remove the heterozygous flies from the vial before their offspring pupate. Why is it

   necessary to remove these flies before you observe your results? _____

   _____

3. **Week 3:** Observe the results of the cross by counting the offspring. Follow the directions on page 108 for anesthetizing and removing flies. When counting, use the stereomicroscope or a hand lens. Divide your flies into those with long wings and those with short (vestigial) wings. Record your results and the class results in Table 9.3.

Table 9.3 Wing Length in *Drosophila*		
	Number of Offspring	
	Long Wings	**Short Wings**
Your data		
Class data		

- Calculate the actual phenotypic ratio you observed. _____ Do your results differ from the expected ratio? _____ Explain. _____

- Do a chi-square test (see Section 9.4 of this laboratory) to determine if the deviation from the expected results can be accounted for by chance alone. Chi-square value: _____

- Repeat these steps using the class data. Do your class data give a ratio that is closer to the expected ratio, and is the chi-square deviation insignificant? _____ Explain. _____

_____

- What phenotypic results are expected for the cross $Ll \times ll$? _____

9.2 Two-Trait Crosses

Two-trait crosses involve two pairs of alleles. Mendel found that during a **dihybrid cross,** when two dihybrid individuals *(AaBb)* reproduce, the phenotypic ratio among the offspring is 9:3:3:1, representing four possible phenotypes. He realized that these results could only be obtained if the alleles of the parents segregated independently of one another when the gametes were formed. From this, Mendel formulated his second law of inheritance:

Law of Independent Assortment

Members of an allelic pair segregate (assort) independently of members of another allelic pair. Therefore, all possible combinations of alleles can occur in the gametes.

Color and Texture of Corn

In corn plants, the allele for purple kernel *(P)* is dominant over the allele for yellow kernel *(p),* and the allele for smooth kernel *(S)* is dominant over the allele for rough kernel *(s)* (Fig. 9.6).

Figure 9.6 Dihybrid cross.
Four types of kernels are seen on an ear of corn following a dihybrid cross: purple smooth, purple rough, yellow smooth, and yellow rough.

20 mm

Experimental Procedure: Color and Texture of Corn

1. Obtain an ear of corn from the supply table. You will be examining the results of the cross *PpSs* × *PpSs*. Complete this Punnett square:

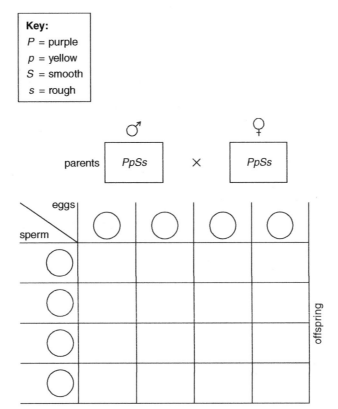

Key:
P = purple
p = yellow
S = smooth
s = rough

parents   PpSs   ×   PpSs

eggs / sperm

offspring

What is the expected phenotypic ratio among the offspring? _____

2. Count the number of kernels of each possible phenotype listed in Table 9.4. Record the sample number and your results in Table 9.4. Use three samples, and total your results for all samples. Also record the class data.

Table 9.4 Color and Texture of Corn				
	Number of Kernels			
	Purple Smooth	**Purple Rough**	**Yellow Smooth**	**Yellow Rough**
Sample # _____				
Sample # _____				
Sample # _____				
Totals				
Class data				

Conclusions: Color and Texture of Corn

- From your data, which two traits seem dominant? _____ and _____

  Which two traits seem recessive? _____ and _____

- Calculate the actual phenotypic ratio you observed. _____ Do your results differ from the

  expected ratio? _____

- Use the chi-square test (see Section 9.4 of this laboratory) to determine if the deviation from the

  expected results can be accounted for by chance alone. Chi-square value: _____

- Repeat these steps using the class data. Do your class data give a ratio that is closer to the expected

  ratio, and is the chi-square deviation insignificant? _____ Explain._____

_____

Wing Length and Body Color in *Drosophila*

In *Drosophila*, long wings *(L)* are dominant over short (vestigial) wings *(l)*, and gray body *(G)* is dominant over ebony (black) body *(g)*. You will be examining the results of the cross *LlGg* × *LlGg*. Complete this Punnett square:

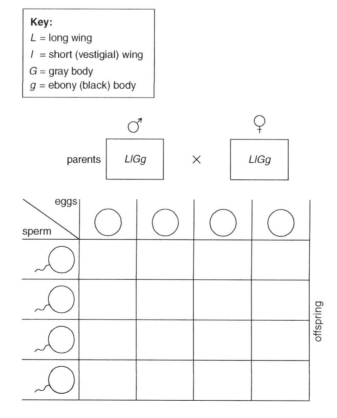

What are the expected phenotypic results of this cross? _____

Experimental Procedure: Wing Length and Body Color in Drosophila

The cross described here will take three weeks. The experiment can be done in one week if your instructor provides you with a vial that already contains the results of the cross *LlGg* × *LlGg*. In this case, proceed directly to week 3. Alternately your instructor may provide you with data. In that case, enter the data into Table 9.5 and proceed directly to the Conclusions.

1. **Week 1:** Place heterozygous flies in a prepared culture vial. Your instructor will show you how to use instant medium and dry yeast to prepare the vial. Label your culture.

    What is the phenotype of heterozygous flies? _____

    What is the genotype of heterozygous flies? _____

2. **Week 2:** Remove the heterozygous flies from the vial before their offspring pupate. Why is it

    necessary to remove these flies before you observe your results? _____

3. **Week 3:** Observe the result of the cross by counting the offspring. Follow the standard directions (see page 108) for anesthetizing and removing flies. Find one fly of each phenotype, and check with the instructor that you have identified them correctly before proceeding. When counting, use the stereomicroscope or a hand lens. Divide your flies into the groups indicated in Table 9.5, and record your results. Also record the class data.

Table 9.5 Wing Length and Body Color in *Drosophila*

	Phenotypes			
	Long Wings Gray Body	Long Wings Ebony Body	Short Wings Gray Body	Short Wings Ebony Body
Number of offspring				
Class data				

Conclusions: Wing Length and Body Color in Drosophila

- Calculate the actual phenotypic ratio you observed. _____ Do your results differ from the expected ratio? _____ Explain. _____

    _____

- Do a chi-square test (see Section 9.4) to determine if the deviation from the expected results can be accounted for by chance alone. Chi-square value: _____

- Repeat these steps using the class data. Do your class data give a ratio that is closer to the expected ratio, and is the chi-square deviation insignificant? _____ Explain. _____

    _____

- In the space provided, do a Punnett square to calculate the expected phenotypic results for the cross *L1Gg* × *l1gg*.

9.3 X-Linked Crosses

In most animals, including fruit flies and humans, males usually have an X and Y chromosome while females have two X chromosomes. Some alleles, called X-linked alleles, occur only on the X chromosome. Males with a normal chromosome inheritance are never heterozygous for X-linked alleles and if they inherit a recessive X-linked alleles, it will be expressed.

Red/White Eye Color in *Drosophila*

In fruit flies, red eyes (X^R) are dominant over white eyes (X^r). You will be examining the results of the cross $X^RY \times X^RX^r$. Complete this Punnett square:

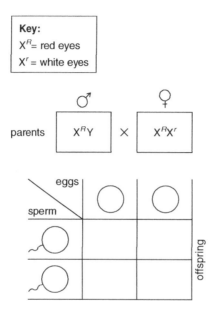

Key:
X^R = red eyes
X^r = white eyes

parents ♂ X^RY × ♀ X^RX^r

eggs

sperm

offspring

What are the expected phenotypic results of this cross?

Females: _____   Males: _____

Experimental Procedure: Red/White Eye Color in Drosophila

The cross described here will take three weeks. The experiment can be done in one week if your instructor provides you with a vial that already contains the results of the cross $X^RY \times X^RX^r$. In this case, proceed directly to week 3. Alternately your instructor may provide you with data. In that case, enter the data into Table 9.6 and proceed directly to the Conclusions.

1. **Week 1:** Place the parental flies ($X^RY \times X^RX^r$) in a prepared culture vial. Your instructor will show you how to use instant medium and dry yeast to prepare the vial. Label your culture.

   What is the phenotype of the female and male flies you are using? _____

   What is the genotype of the female flies? _____

   What is the genotype of the male flies? _____

2. Week 2: Remove the parental flies from the vial before their offspring pupate. Why is it necessary to remove these flies before you observe your results? _____

_____

3. Week 3: Observe the results of the cross by counting the offspring. Follow the standard directions (see page 108) for anesthetizing and removing flies. When counting, use the stereomicroscope or a hand lens. Divide your flies into the following groups: (1) red-eyed males, (2) red-eyed females, (3) white-eyed males, and (4) white-eyed females. Record your results in Table 9.6. Also record the class data.

Table 9.6 Red/White Eye Color in *Drosophila*		
	Number of Offspring	
Your Data:	**Red Eyes**	**White Eyes**
Males		
Females		
Class Data:		
Males		
Females		

Conclusions: Red/White Eye Color in Drosophila

- Calculate the actual phenotypic ratio you observed for males and females separately.

  Males: _____

  Females: _____

- Do your results differ from the expected results? _____

- Do a chi-square test (see Section 9.4) to determine if the deviation from the expected results can be accounted for by chance alone. Chi-square value: _____

- Repeat these steps using the class data. Do your class data give a ratio that is closer to the expected ratio, and is the chi-square deviation insignificant? _____ Explain. _____

_____

- In the space provided, do a Punnett square to calculate the expected phenotypic results for the cross $X^R Y \times X^r X^r$.

9.4 Chi-Square Analysis

Your experimental results can be evaluated using the **chi-square** (χ^2) test. This is the statistical test most frequently used to determine whether data obtained experimentally provide a "good fit," or approximation, to the expected or theoretical data. Basically, the chi-square test can determine whether any deviations from the expected values are due to chance. Chance alone can cause the actual observed ratio to vary somewhat from the calculated ratio for a genetic cross. For example, a ratio of exactly 3:1 for a monohybrid cross is only rarely observed. Actual results will differ, but at some point, the difference is so great as to be unexpected. The chi-square test indicates this point. After this point, the original hypothesis (for example, that a monohybrid cross gives a 3:1 ratio) is not supported by the data.

The formula for the test is $\chi^2 = \Sigma(d^2/e)$

where χ^2 = chi-square

Σ = sum of

d = difference between expected and observed results (most often termed the *deviation*)

e = expected results

For example, in a one-trait cross involving fruit flies with long wings (dominant) and fruit flies with short wings (recessive), a 3:1 ratio is expected in the second generation (F_2). Therefore, if you count 160 flies, 40 are expected to have short wings, and 120 are expected to have long wings. But if you count 44 short-winged flies and 116 long-winged flies, then the value for the chi-square test would be as calculated in Table 9.7.

Table 9.7 Calculation of Chi-Square (Example)

Phenotype	Observed Number	Expected Results (e)	Difference (d)	d^2	Partial Chi-Square (d^2/e)
Short wings	44	40	4	16	16/40 = 0.400
Long wings	116	120	4	16	16/120 = 0.133
					Chi-square = $\chi^2 = \Sigma(d^2/e)$ = 0.400 + 0.133 = 0.533

Now look up this chi-square value (χ^2) in a table that indicates whether the probability *(p)* is that the differences noted are due only to chance in the form of random sampling error or whether the results should be explained on the basis of a different prediction (hypothesis). In Table 9.8, the notation C refers to the number of "classes," which in this laboratory would be determined by the number of phenotypic traits studied. The example involves two classes: short wings and long wings. However, as indicated in the table by $C-1$, it is necessary to subtract 1 from the total number of classes. In the example, $C-1 = 1$. Therefore, the χ^2 value (0.533) would fall in the first line of Table 9.8 between 0.455 and 1.074. These correspond with p values of 0.50 and 0.30, respectively. This means that, by random chance, this difference between the actual count and the expected count would occur between 30% and 50% of the time. In biology, it is generally accepted that a p value greater than 0.10 is acceptable and that a p value lower than 0.10 indicates that the results cannot be due to random sampling and therefore do not support (do not "fit") the original prediction (hypothesis). A chi-square analysis is used to *refute* (falsify) a hypothesis, not to *prove* it.

Table 9.8 Values of Chi-Square

	Hypothesis is Supported						Hypothesis is Not Supported			
	Differences Are Insignificant						Differences Are Significant			
p	0.99	0.95	0.80	0.50	0.30	0.20	0.10	0.05	0.02	0.01
$C-1$										
1	0.00016	0.0039	0.064	0.455	1.074	1.642	2.706	3.841	5.412	6.635
2	0.0201	0.103	0.446	1.386	2.408	3.219	4.605	5.991	7.824	9.210
3	0.115	0.352	1.005	2.366	3.665	4.642	6.251	7.815	9.837	11.345
4	0.297	0.711	1.649	3.357	4.878	5.989	7.779	9.488	11.668	13.277
5	0.554	1.145	2.343	4.351	6.064	7.289	9.236	11.070	13.388	15.086

Source: Data from W. T. Keeton, et al., *Laboratory Guide for Biological Science,* 1968, p. 189.

Use Table 9.9 for performing a chi-square analysis of your results from a previous Experimental Procedure in this laboratory. If you performed a one-trait (monohybrid) cross, you will use only the first two lines. If you performed a two-trait (dihybrid) cross, you will use four lines.

$\chi^2 =$ _____

$C-1 =$ _____

p (from Table 9.8) $=$ _____

Table 9.9 Calculation of Chi-Square

Phenotype	Observed Number	Expected Results (e)	Difference (d)	d^2	Partial Chi-Square (d^2/e)
					=
					=
					=
					=
				Chi-square $= \chi^2 = \Sigma(d^2/e) =$	

Conclusions: Chi-Square Analysis

- Do your results support your original prediction? _____

- If not, how can you account for this? _____

_____

Laboratory Review 9

1. If offspring exhibit a 3:1 phenotypic ratio, what are the genotypes of the parents? _____

2. In fruit flies, which of the characteristics that you studied was X-linked? _____

3. If offspring exhibit a 9:3:3:1 phenotypic ratio, what are the genotypes of the parents?

_____

_____

4. If the F_2 generation consists of 90 long-winged flies to 30 short-winged flies, what was the phenotype of the F_1 flies? _____

_____

5. Briefly describe the life cycle of *Drosophila*. _____

_____

_____

6. When doing a genetic cross, why is it necessary to remove parent flies before the pupae have hatched?

_____

7. What is the genotype of a white-eyed male fruit fly? _____

8. Suppose you counted 40 green tobacco seedlings and 2 white tobacco seedlings in one agar plate. According to the chi-square test, do your results support the hypothesis that both parent plants were

heterozygous for the color allele? _____

9. Suppose you counted tobacco seedlings in six agar plates, and your data were as follows: 125 green plants and 39 white plants. According to the chi-square test, are your deviations from the expected

values due to chance? _____

10. Suppose that students in the laboratory periods before yours removed some of the purple and yellow corn kernels on the ears of corn as they were performing the Experimental Procedure. What effect would this have on your results?

_____

_____

Biology Website

The companion website for *Biology* provides a wealth of information organized and integrated by chapter. You will find practice tests, animations, videos, and much more that will complement your learning and understanding of general biology.

www.mhhe.com/maderbiology10

McGraw-Hill Access Science Website

An Encyclopedia of Science and Technology Online which provides more information including videos that can enhance the laboratory experience.

www.accessscience.com

10

Human Genetics

Learning Outcomes

10.1 Chromosomal Inheritance
- Explain how nondisjunction occurs and which numerical sex chromosome abnormalities may result from nondisjunction.   120–23

10.2 Genetic Inheritance
- Determine students' genotypes by observing themselves and their relatives.   124–25
- Solve genetics problems involving autosomal dominant, autosomal recessive, and X-linked recessive alleles. 125–28
- Determine whether a pedigree represents a pattern of autosomal dominant, autosomal recessive, or X-linked recessive inheritance.   128–30

Introduction

Our study of human genetics in this laboratory first concerns the inheritance of an abnormal chromosome number (see also page 98). Figure 10.1 contrasts a normal karyotype with an abnormal one. As you can see, the abnormal karyotype has three number 21 chromosomes instead of two number 21 chromosomes. Therefore, this individual has trisomy 21 (Down syndrome), the most common autosomal trisomy in humans. An eyelid fold; a flat face, stubby fingers; a large fissured tongue, and usually some degree of mental retardation characterize Down syndrome. While Down syndrome is an autosomal syndrome, our laboratory concentrates on syndromes due to an abnormal sex chromosome number.

Next, we consider autosomal dominant and recessive traits in human beings before moving on to recessive X-linked traits. We will have the opportunity to observe that Mendel's laws apply not only to peas and fruit flies, they also apply to humans. This laboratory provides an opportunity to practice genetics problems. Finally, we will learn how to read and construct a pedigree, which is a diagram showing the inheritance of a genetic disorder within a family. Genetic counselors use pedigrees to counsel couples about the chances of passing a genetic disorder to their children.

Figure 10.1   Normal versus abnormal human karyotype.
a. A normal karyotype has 22 pairs of autosomes and one pair of sex chromosomes. **b.** A person with Down syndrome has an abnormal karyotype with three number 21 chromosomes.

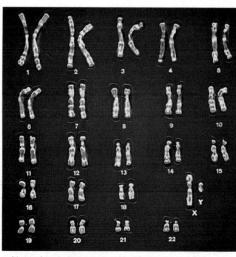
a. Normal male karyotype with 46 chromosomes.

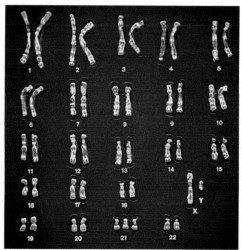
b. Down syndrome karyotype with an extra chromosome 21.

10.1 Chromosomal Inheritance

Usually, gametogenesis and fertilization occur normally, and an individual inherits 22 pairs of autosomes and one pair of sex chromosomes (see Fig. 10.1*a*). Gametogenesis involves meiosis, the type of cell division that reduces the chromosome number by one-half because the homologues separate during meiosis I. When homologues fail to separate during meiosis I, called **nondisjunction**, gametes with too few (n − 1) or too many (n + 1) chromosomes result. Nondisjunction can also occur during meiosis II if the chromatids fail to separate and the daughter chromosomes go into the same daughter cell. Again, the gametes will have too few or too many chromosomes. Therefore, nondisjunction leads to various syndromes because the individual has inherited an abnormal number of chromosomes (see Fig. 10.1*b*).

Syndromes Due to Numerical Sex Chromosome Abnormalities

A female with **Turner syndrome** (XO) has only one sex chromosome, an X chromosome; the O signifies the absence of the second sex chromosome. Because the ovaries never become functional, these females do not undergo puberty or menstruation, and their breasts do not develop. Generally, females with Turner syndrome have a short build, folds of skin on the back of the neck, difficulty recognizing various spatial patterns, and normal intelligence. With hormone supplements, they can lead fairly normal lives.

When an egg having two X chromosomes is fertilized by an X-bearing sperm, an individual with **poly-X syndrome** results. The body cells have three X chromosomes and therefore 47 chromosomes. Although they tend to have learning disabilities, poly-X females have no apparent physical abnormalities, and many are fertile and have children with a normal chromosome count.

When an egg having two X chromosomes is fertilized by a Y-bearing sperm, a male with **Klinefelter syndrome** results. This individual is male in general appearance, but the testes are underdeveloped, and the breasts may be enlarged. The limbs of XXY males tend to be longer than average, muscular development is poor, body hair is sparse, and many XXY males have learning disabilities.

Jacob syndrome can be due to nondisjunction during meiosis II of spermatogenesis. These males are usually taller than average, suffer from persistent acne, and tend to have speech and reading problems. At one time, it was suggested that XYY males were likely to be criminally aggressive, but the incidence of such behavior has been shown to be no greater than that among normal XY males.

Complete Table 10.1 to show how a physician would recognize each of these syndromes from a karyotype.

Table 10.1 Numerical Sex Chromosome Abnormalities

Syndrome Number	Comparison with Normal Number
Turner:	Normal Female:
Poly-X:	Normal Female:
Klinefelter:	Normal Male:
Jacob:	Normal Male:

Experimental Procedure: Gametogensis and Nondisjunction*

Gametogenesis in females is called **oogenesis** (egg production) and in males is called **spermatogenesis** (sperm production) (see page 99).

Building the Chromosomes

1. Obtain the following materials: 36 red pop beads, 26 blue (or green) pop beads, and eight magnetic centromeres.
2. Build four duplicated sex chromosomes (3 Xs and 1 Y) as follows:

   Two red X chromosomes: Each chromatid will have nine red pop beads. Place the centromeres so that two beads are above each centromere and seven beads are below each centromere. Bring the centromeres together.

   One blue X chromosome: Each chromatid will have nine blue pop beads. Place the centromere so that two beads are above each centromere and seven beads are below each centromere. Bring the centromeres together.

   Y chromosome: Each chromatid will have four blue pop beads. Place the centromeres so that two beads are above each centromere and two beads are below each centromere. Bring the centromeres together.

Simulating Meiosis During Normal Oogenesis

Place one blue X and one red X chromosome together in the middle of your work area. (The blue X chromosome came from the father, and the red X chromosome came from the mother.) Have the chromosomes go through meiosis I and meiosis II. What is the sex chromosome constitution of each of the four meiotic products? Each egg has _____ (number) _____ (type) chromosome(s).

Simulating Meiosis During Normal Spermatogenesis

Place a red X and a blue Y chromosome together in the middle of your work area. (The red X chromosome came from the mother, and the blue Y chromosome came from the father.) Have the chromosomes go through meiosis I and meiosis II. What is the chromosome constitution of each of the four meiotic products? Two sperm have one _____ sex chromosome, and two sperm have one _____ sex chromosome.

Simulating Fertilization

In the Punnett square provided here, fill in the products of fertilization using the *type* of gamete that resulted from normal oogenesis and the *types* of gametes that resulted from normal spermatogenesis. (Disregard the color of the chromosomes.)

---

*Exercise courtesy of Victoria Finnerty, Sue Jinks-Robertson, and Gregg Orloff of Emory University, Atlanta, GA.

Figure 10.2 Nondisjunction of sex chromosomes.

a. Nondisjunction during oogenesis produces the types of eggs shown. Fertilization with normal sperm results in the syndromes noted. (Nonviable means existence is not possible.) **b.** Nondisjunction during meiosis I of spermatogenesis results in the types of sperm shown. Fusion with normal eggs results in the syndromes noted. Nondisjunction during meiosis II of spermatogenesis results in the types of sperm shown. Fusion with normal eggs results in the syndromes shown.

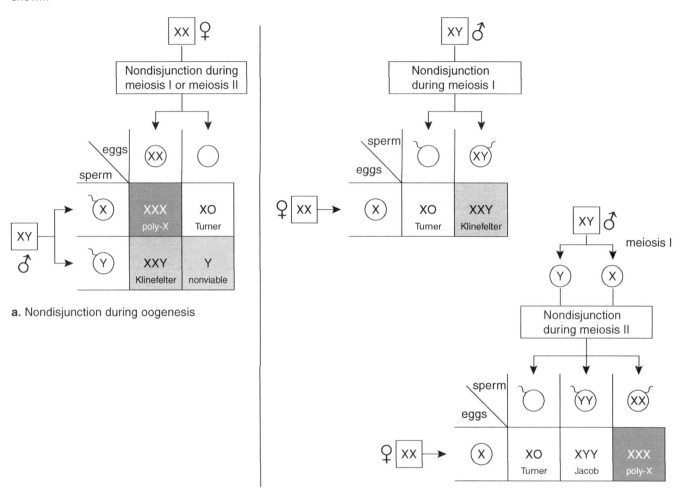

a. Nondisjunction during oogenesis

b. Nondisjunction during spermatogenesis

Simulating Nondisjunction During Meiosis I

1. Simulate meiosis during normal oogenesis and spermatogenesis as before, except as follows. Assume that nondisjunction occurs during meiosis I, but the chromatids separate at the centromere during meiosis II (Fig. 10.2a). What is the sex chromosome constitution of each of the four meiotic products:

   for oogenesis? ◯ ◯ ◯ ◯   for spermatogenesis? ♂◯ ♂◯ ◯ ◯

   Further note that each egg having chromosomes has one _____ (color) chromosome and one _____ (color) chromosome.

2. In the space provided here, draw a Punnett square, and fill in the products of fertilization using (a) normal sperm × *types* of abnormal eggs as in Figure 10.2*a*, and (b) normal egg × *types* of abnormal sperm, as in Figure 10.2*b* for nondisjunction during meiosis I. (Disregard the color of the chromosomes.)

   a.   b.

Conclusions: Nondisjunction During Meiosis I

- What syndromes are the result of (a)? _____
- Are all offspring viable (capable of living)? _____ Explain. _____

   _____

- What syndromes are the result of (b)? _____
- Are all offspring viable? _____ Explain. _____

Simulating Nondisjunction During Meiosis II

1. Simulate meiosis during normal oogenesis and spermatogenesis as before, except as follows. Assume that meiosis I is normal, but the chromatids of the chromosomes fail to separate during meiosis II. What is the sex chromosome constitution of each of the four meiotic products:

   for oogenesis? ◯ ◯ ◯ ◯   for spermatogenesis? ◗ ◗ ◗ ◗

2. In the space provided here, draw a Punnett square, and fill in the products of fertilization using (a) normal sperm × *types* of abnormal eggs, as in Figure 10.2*a*, and (b) normal egg × *types* of abnormal sperm, as in Figure 10.2*b* for nondisjunction during meiosis II.

   a.   b.

Conclusions: Nondisjunction During Meiosis II

- What syndromes are the result of (a)? _____
- Are all offspring viable? _____ Explain. _____

   _____

- What syndromes are the result of (b)? _____
- Are all offspring viable? _____ Explain. _____

   _____

10.2 Genetic Inheritance

Just as we inherit pairs of chromosomes, we inherit pairs of alleles, alternate forms of a gene. As before, a **dominant allele** is assigned a capital letter, while a **recessive allele** is given the same letter lowercased.

The **genotype** tells the alleles of the individual, while the **phenotype** describes the appearance of the individual.

Autosomal Dominant and Recessive Traits

The alleles for autosomal traits are carried on the nonsex chromosomes. If individuals are homozygous dominant (*AA*) or heterozygous (*Aa*), their phenotype is the dominant trait. If individuals are homozygous recessive (*aa*), their phenotype is the recessive trait.

Experimental Procedure: Autosomal Traits

1. For this Experimental Procedure, you will need a lab partner to help you determine your phenotype for the traits listed in the first column of Table 10.2. Figure 10.3 illustrates some of these traits. Record your phenotypes by circling them in the first column of the table.

Figure 10.3 Examples of human phenotypes.

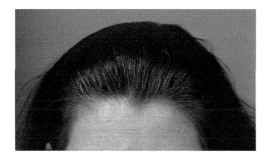
Widow's peak

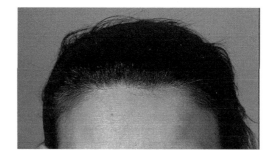
Straight hairline

Bent little finger

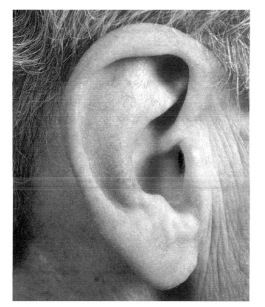
Unattached earlobes

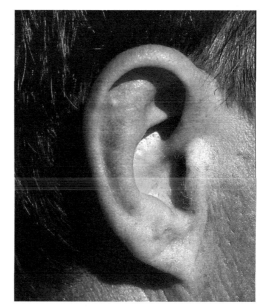
Attached earlobes

Straight little finger

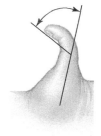
Hitchhiker's thumb

2. Determine your probable genotype. If you have the recessive phenotype, you know your genotype. If you have the dominant phenotype, you may be able to decide whether you are homozygous dominant or heterozygous by recalling the phenotype of your parents, siblings, or children. Circle your probable genotype in the second column of Table 10.2.

3. Your instructor will tally the class's phenotypes for each trait so that you can complete the third column of Table 10.2.

4. Complete Table 10.2 by calculating the percentage of the class with each trait. Are dominant phenotypes always the most common in a population? _____ Explain. _____

_____

Table 10.2 Autosomal Human Traits

Trait: d = Dominant r = Recessive	Possible Genotypes	Number in Class	Percentage of Class with Trait

Hairline:
    Widow's peak (d)
    Straight hairline (r)
	WW or Ww
	ww
		_____	

Earlobes:
    Unattached (d)
    Attached (r)
	EE or Ee
	ee
		_____	

Skin pigmentation:
    Freckles (d)
    No freckles (r)
	FF or Ff
	ff
		_____	

Hair on back of hand:
    Present (d)
    Absent (r)
	HH or Hh
	hh
		_____	

Thumb hyperextension—"hitchhiker's thumb":
    Last segment cannot be bent backward (d)
    Last segment can be bent back to 60° (r)
	TT or Tt
	tt
		_____	

Bent little finger:
    Little finger bends toward ring finger (d)
    Straight little finger (r)
	LL or Ll
	ll
		_____	

Interlacing of fingers:
    Left thumb over right (d)
    Right thumb over left (r)
	II or Ii
	ii
		_____	

Genetics Problems Involving the Traits in Table 10.2

1. Nancy and the members of her immediate family have attached earlobes. Her maternal grandfather has unattached earlobes. What is the genotype of her maternal grandfather?_____ Nancy's maternal grandmother is no longer living. What could have been the genotype of her maternal grandmother? _____

Figure 10.4 Two common patterns of autosomal inheritance in humans.

Left: Both parents are heterozygous. *Right:* One parent is heterozygous and the other is homozygous recessive.

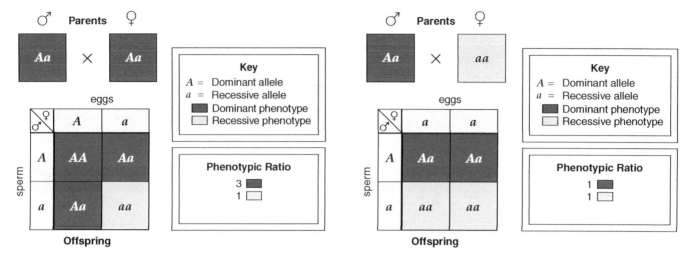

See Figure 10.4 (*left*) for questions 2 and 3:

2. Joe does not have a bent little finger, but his parents do. What is the expected phenotypic ratio among the parents' children? _____

3. Henry is adopted. He has hair on the back of his hand. Could both of his parents have had hair on the back of the hand? _____ Could both of his parents have had no hair on the back of the hand? _____ Explain. _____

_____

_____

Genetics Problems Involving Genetic Disorders

See Figure 10.4 (*left*) for questions 1 and 2:

1. Cystic fibrosis is an autosomal recessive disorder. If both of Sally's parents are heterozygous for cystic fibrosis, what are her chances of inheriting cystic fibrosis? _____

2. Nancy has cystic fibrosis, but neither parent has cystic fibrosis. What is the genotype of all people involved? _____

See Figure 10.4 (*right*) for questions 3 and 4:

3. Huntington disease is an autosomal dominant disorder. If only one of Sam's parents is heterozygous for Huntington disease and the other is homozygous recessive, what are his chances of inheriting Huntington disease? _____

4. In Henry's family, only his father has Huntington disease. What are the genotypes of Henry, his mother, and his father? _____

Sex Linkage

The sex chromosomes carry genes that affect traits other than the individual's sex. Genes on the sex chromosomes are called **sex-linked genes.** The vast majority of sex-linked genes have alleles on the X chromosome and are called **X-linked genes.** Most often, the abnormal condition is recessive.

Color blindness is an X-linked, recessive trait. The possible genotypes and phenotypes are as follows:

Females
$X^B X^B$ = normal vision
$X^B X^b$ = normal vision (carrier)
$X^b X^b$ = color blindness

Males
$X^B Y$ = normal vision
$X^b Y$ = color blindness

Experimental Procedure: X-Linked Traits

1. Your instructor will provide you with a color blindness chart. Have your lab partner present the chart to you. Write down the words or symbols you see, but do not allow your partner to see what you write, and do not discuss what you see. This is important because color-blind people see something different than do people who are not color blind.
2. Now test your lab partner as he or she has tested you.
3. Are you color blind? _____ If so, what is your genotype? _____
4. If you are a female and are not color blind, you can judge whether you are homozygous or heterozygous by knowing if any member of your family is color blind. If your father is color blind,

   what is your genotype? _____ If your mother is color blind, what is your genotype? _____

   If you know of no one in your family who is color blind, what is your probable genotype? _____

Genetics Problems Involving X-Linked Genetic Disorders

See Figure 10.5 (*left*) for questions 1 and 2 :

1. If a father is color blind, what are the chances his daughters will be color blind? _____

   Be carriers? _____

2. Mary Jo is a carrier for hemophilia, an X-linked recessive disorder. Her mother is perfectly normal.

   What is her father's genotype? _____

Figure 10.5   Two common patterns of X-linked inheritance in humans.
Left: A color-blind father has carrier daughters. *Right:* The sons of a carrier mother have a 50% chance of being color blind.

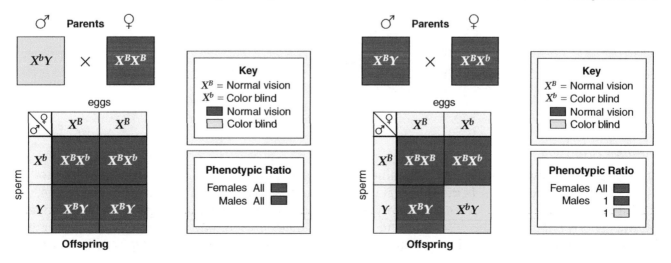

See Figure 10.5 (*right*) for questions 3 and 4 :

3. If a boy is color blind, from which parent did he inherit the defective allele? _____

4. Mary has a color-blind son but Mary and both of Mary's parents have normal vision. Give the genotype of all people involved. _____

5. A person with Klinefelter syndrome is color blind. Both his father and mother have normal vision, but his maternal uncle is color blind. In which parent and at what meiotic division did sex chromosome nondisjunction occur? _____

   (*Hint:* Use Figure 10.2 to help solve this problem.)

6. A person with Turner syndrome has hemophilia. Her mother does not have hemophilia, but her father does. In which parent did nondisjunction occur, considering that the single X came from the father? _____ Is it possible to tell if nondisjunction occurred during meiosis I or meiosis II? _____ Explain. _____

   _____

   (*Hint:* Use Figure 10.2 to help solve this problem.)

Pedigrees

A **pedigree** shows the inheritance of a genetic disorder within a family and can help determine whether any particular individual has an allele for that disorder. Then a Punnett square can be done to determine the chances of a couple producing an affected child.

In a pedigree, Roman numerals indicate the generation, and Arabic numerals indicate particular individuals in that generation. The symbols used to indicate normal and affected males and females, reproductive partners, and siblings are shown in Figure 10.6.

Figure 10.6. Pedigree symbols.

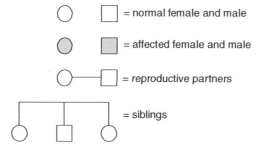

Pedigree Analyses

For each of the following pedigrees, determine how a genetic disorder is passed. Use Table 10.3 to help with this determination. Is the inheritance pattern autosomal dominant, autosomal recessive, or X-linked recessive? Also, decide the genotype of particular individuals in the pedigree. Remember that the *genotype* indicates the dominant and recessive alleles present and the *phenotype* is the actual physical appearance of the trait in the individual. A pedigree indicates the phenotype, and you can reason out the genotype.

Table 10.3 Pedigree Solution Chart

Inheritance Pattern	Notes	Clues	Possible Genotypes
Autosomal dominant (any chromosome except X or Y)	If at least one chromosome has the allele, the individual will be affected.	One or both parents are affected. Many of the children are affected.	AA or Aa = affected aa = normal
Autosomal recessive (any chromosome except X or Y)	Both chromosomes must have the recessive allele for the individual to be affected.	Neither parent is affected. Few of the children are affected.	AA or Aa = normal Aa = carrier* aa = affected
X-linked recessive (only the X chromosome)	The trait is only carried on the X chromosome. There must be a recessive allele on the X chromosome for the trait to be expressed.	Trait is primarily found in males. It is often passed from grandfather to grandson.	X^AX^A and X^AX^a = normal female; X^AX^a = carrier female* X^AY = normal male X^aX^a = affected female X^aY = affected male

*A carrier is one who does not show the trait but has the ability to pass it on to his or her offspring.

1. Study the following pedigree:

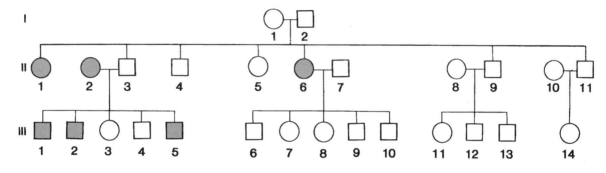

a. What is the inheritance pattern for this genetic disorder? _____

b. What is the genotype of the following individuals? Use *A* for the dominant allele and *a* for the recessive allele.

Generation I, individual 1: _____

Generation II, individual 1: _____

Generation III, individual 8: _____

2. Study the following pedigree:

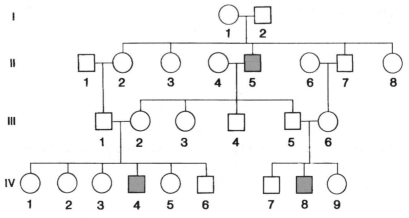

a. What is the inheritance pattern for this genetic disorder? _____

b. What is the genotype of the following individuals?

Generation I, individual 1: _____

Generation II, individual 8: _____

Generation III, individual 1: _____

Construction of a Pedigree

You are a genetic counselor who has been given the following information from which you will construct a pedigree.

1. Your data: Henry has a double row of eyelashes, which is a dominant trait. Both his maternal grandfather and his mother have double eyelashes. Their spouses are normal. Henry is married to Isabella and their first child Polly has normal eyelashes. The couple wants to know the chances of any child having a double row of eyelashes.

2. *Construct two blank pedigrees.* Begin with the maternal grandfather and grandmother and end with Polly.

Pedigree 1   **Pedigree 2**

3. Pedigree 1: Try out a pattern of autosomal dominant inheritance by assigning appropriate genotypes for an autosomal dominant pattern of inheritance to each person in this pedigree. Pedigree 2: Try out a pattern of X-linked dominant inheritance by assigning appropriate genotypes for this pattern

   of inheritance to each person in your pedigree. Which pattern is correct? _____

4. What is your key for this trait?

   Key: _____ normal eyelashes   _____ double row of eyelashes

5. Use correct genotypes to show a cross between Henry and Isabella and calculate the expected phenotypic ratio among the offspring:

   Henry   Isabella

   _____ X _____

6. What are the percentage chances of Henry and Isabella having a child with double eyelashes? _____

Laboratory Review 10

1. Name one pair of chromosomes not homologous in a normal karyotype. _____

2. A woman is heterozygous. Which one could produce an egg in which two X chromosomes carry an allele for the recessive trait color blindness: nondisjunction during meiosis I or nondisjunction during meiosis II? _____

   Explain. _____

3. Which one could produce a sperm with two X chromosomes: nondisjunction during meiosis I or nondisjunction during meiosis II? _____

   Explain. _____

4. If an individual exhibits the dominant trait, do you know the genotype? _____

   Why or why not? _____

   _____

5. A son is color blind, but both parents are normal. Give the genotype of the mother _____ and the father _____. Explain the pattern of inheritance. _____

   _____

6. What pattern of inheritance in a pedigree would allow you to decide that a trait is X-linked?

   _____

7. What pattern of inheritance in a pedigree would allow you to decide that a trait is autosomal recessive?

   _____

8. What is the difference between a Punnett square and a pedigree? _____

   _____

9. What is the probability
   a. two individuals with an autosomal recessive trait will have a child with the same trait?

      _____

   b. a woman heterozygous for an X-linked trait will have a son with a genetic disorder if the genetic disorder is recessive? _____ If the genetic disorder is dominant? _____

   c. a woman whose father was color blind will have a son who is color blind?

Biology **Website**

The companion website for *Biology* provides a wealth of information organized and integrated by chapter. You will find practice tests, animations, videos, and much more that will complement your learning and understanding of general biology.

www.mhhe.com/maderbiology10

McGraw-Hill Access Science Website

An Encyclopedia of Science and Technology Online which provides more information including videos that can enhance the laboratory experience.

www.accessscience.com

LABORATORY

11

DNA Biology and Technology

Learning Outcomes

11.1 DNA Structure and Replication
- Explain how the structure of DNA facilitates replication.   134–35
- Explain how DNA replication is semiconservative.   136

11.2 RNA Structure
- List the ways in which RNA structure differs from DNA structure.   137–38

11.3 DNA and Protein Synthesis
- Describe how DNA is able to store information.   138–41
- State the function of transcription and translation during protein synthesis.   139–41

11.4 Isolation of DNA
- Describe the procedure for isolation of DNA.   142

11.5 Genetic Disorders
- Understand the relationship between abnormal DNA base sequence and a genetic disorder.   143–44
- Understand the process of gel electrophoresis.   144–45

Introduction

This laboratory pertains to molecular genetics and biotechnology. Molecular genetics is the study of the structure and function of **DNA (deoxyribonucleic acid),** the genetic material. Biotechnology is the manipulation of DNA for the benefit of human beings and other organisms.

First we will study the structure of DNA and see how that structure facilitates DNA replication in the nucleus of cells. DNA replicates prior to cell division; following cell division, each daughter cell has a complete copy of the genetic material. DNA replication is also needed to pass genetic material from one generation to the next. You may have an opportunity to use models to see how replication occurs.

Then we will study the structure of **RNA (ribonucleic acid)** and how it differs from that of DNA, before examining how DNA, with the help of RNA, specifies protein synthesis. The linear construction of DNA, in which nucleotide follows nucleotide, is paralleled by the linear construction of the primary structure of protein, in which amino acid follows amino acid. Essentially, we will see that the sequence of nucleotides in DNA codes for the sequence of amino acids in a protein. We will also review the role of three types of RNA in protein synthesis. DNA's code is passed to messenger RNA (mRNA), which moves to the ribosomes containing ribosomal RNA (rRNA). Transfer RNA (tRNA) brings the amino acids to the ribosomes, and they become sequenced in the order directed by mRNA.

We now understand that a mutated gene has an altered DNA base sequence, which can lead to a genetic disorder. You will have an opportunity to carry out a laboratory procedure that detects whether an individual is normal, has sickle-cell disease, or is a carrier.

11.1 DNA Structure and Replication

The structure of DNA lends itself to **replication,** the process that makes a copy of a DNA molecule. DNA replication is a necessary part of chromosome duplication, which precedes cell division. It also makes possible the passage of DNA from one generation to the next.

DNA Structure

DNA is a polymer of nucleotide monomers (Fig. 11.1). Each nucleotide is composed of three molecules: deoxyribose (a 5-carbon sugar), a phosphate, and a nitrogen-containing base.

Figure 11.1 Overview of DNA structure.
Diagram of DNA double helix shows that the molecule resembles a twisted ladder. Sugar-phosphate backbones make up the sides of the ladder, and hydrogen-bonded bases make up the rungs of the ladder. Complementary base pairing dictates that A is bonded to T and G is bonded to C and vice versa. *Label the boxed nucleotide pair as directed in the next Observation.*

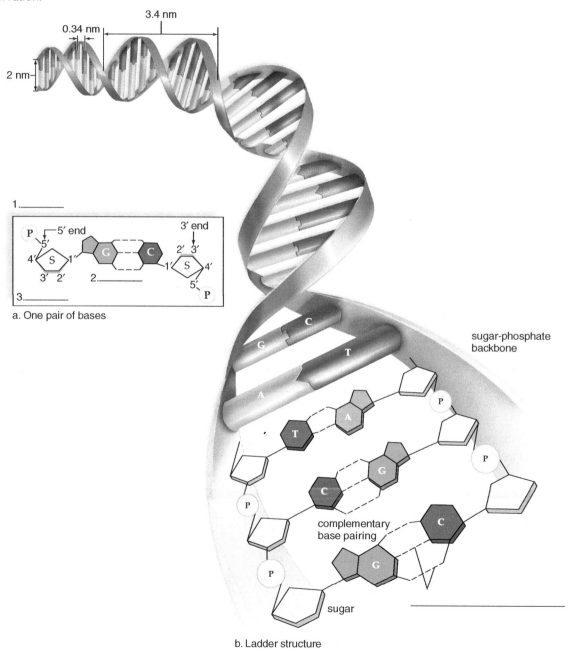

a. One pair of bases

b. Ladder structure

1. A boxed nucleotide pair is shown in Figure 11.1a. If you are working with a kit, draw a representation of one of your nucleotides here. *Label phosphate, base pair, and deoxyribose in your drawing and 1–3 in Figure 11.1a.*

2. Notice the four types of bases: cytosine (C), thymine (T), adenine (A), and guanine (G). What is the color of each of the four types of bases in Figure 11.1? In your kit? Complete Table 11.1 by writing in the colors of the bases.

Table 11.1   Base Colors

	In Figure 11.1*b*	In Your Kit
Cytosine		
Thymine		
Adenine		
Guanine		

3. Using Figure 11.1 as a guide, join several nucleotides together. Observe the entire DNA molecule. What type of molecules make up the backbone (uprights of ladder) of DNA (Fig. 11.1*b*)? _____ and _____ In the backbone, the phosphate of one nucleotide is bonded to a sugar of the next nucleotide.

4. Using Figure 11.1 as a guide, join the bases together with hydrogen bonds. Label a hydrogen bond in Figure 11.1. Dashes are used to represent hydrogen bonds in Figure 11.1*b* because hydrogen bonds are (strong or weak). _____

5. Notice in Figure 11.1*b* and in your model, that the base A is always paired with the base _____, and the base C is always paired with the base _____. This is called complementary base pairing.

6. In Figure 11.1*b*, what molecules make up the rungs of the ladder? _____

7. Each half of the DNA molecule is a DNA strand. Why is DNA also called a double helix (Fig. 11.1*b*)?

_____

DNA Replication

During replication, the DNA molecule is duplicated so that there are two DNA molecules. We will see that complementary base pairing makes replication possible.

Observation: DNA Replication

1. Before replication begins, DNA is unzipped. Using Figure 11.2a as a guide, break apart your two DNA strands. What bonds are broken in order to unzip the DNA strands? _____

2. Using Figure 11.2b as a guide, attach new complementary nucleotides to each strand using complementary base pairing.

3. Show that you understand complementary base pairing by completing Table 11.2. You now have two DNA molecules (Fig. 11.2c). Are your molecules identical? _____

4. Because of complementary base pairing, each new double helix is composed of an _____ strand and a _____ strand. *Write old or new in 1–10, Figure 11.2a, b, and c. Conservative* means to save something from the past. Why is DNA replication called semiconservative?

_____
_____
_____
_____

Figure 11.2 DNA replication.
Use of the ladder configuration better illustrates how replication takes place. **a.** The parental DNA molecule. **b.** The "old" strands of the parental DNA molecule have separated. New complementary nucleotides available in the cell are pairing with those of each old strand. **c.** Replication is complete.

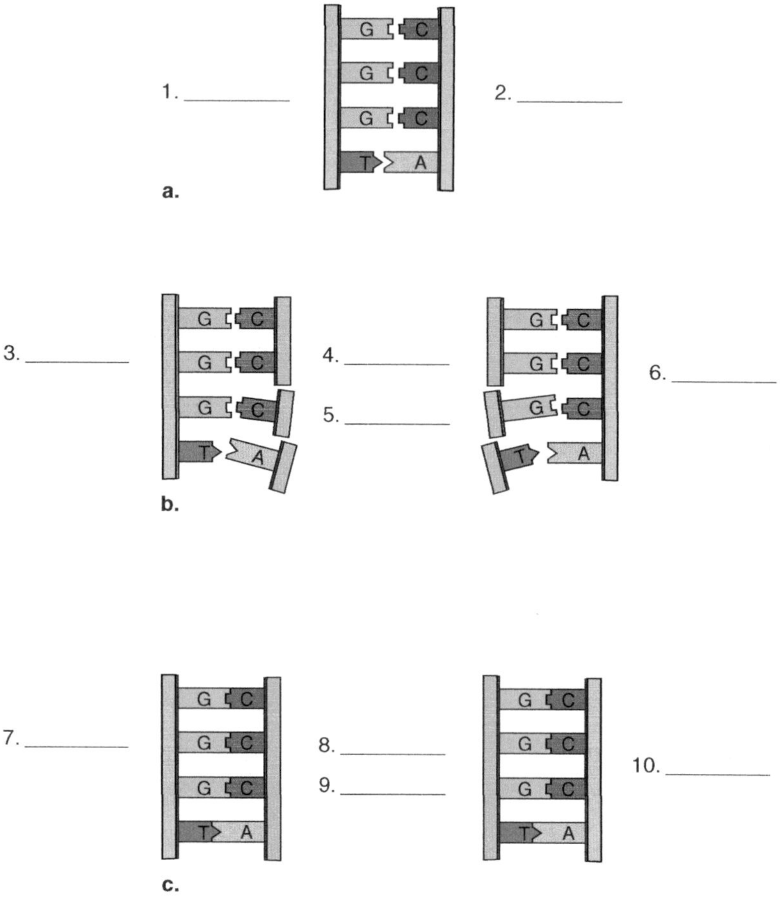

5. Genetic material has to be inherited from cell to cell and organism to organism. Consider that because of DNA replication, a chromosome is composed of two chromatids and each chromatid is a DNA double helix. The chromatids separate during cell division so that each daughter cell receives a copy of each chromosome. Does replication provide a means for passing DNA from cell to cell and organism to organism?

_____

Explain. _____

_____

Table 11.2 DNA Replication																											
Old strand	G	G	G	T	T	C	C	A	T	T	A	A	A	T	T	C	C	A	G	A	A	A	T	C	A	T	A
New strand																											

11.2 RNA Structure

Like DNA, RNA is a polymer of nucleotides (Fig. 11.3). In an RNA nucleotide, the sugar ribose is attached to a phosphate molecule and to a nitrogen-containing base, C, U, A, or G. In RNA, the base uracil replaces thymine as one of the pyrimidine bases. RNA is single stranded, whereas DNA is double stranded.

Figure 11.3   Overview of RNA structure.
RNA is a single strand of nucleotides. *Label the boxed nucleotide as directed in the next Observation.*

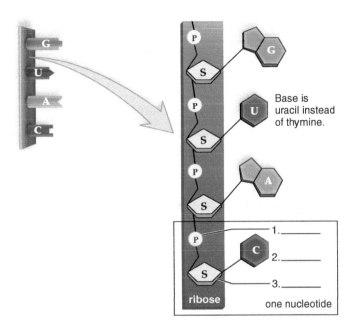

1. Describe the backbone of an RNA molecule. _____

2. Where are the bases located in an RNA molecule? _____

3. Complete Table 11.3 to show the complementary DNA bases for the RNA bases.

Table 11.3 DNA and RNA Bases				
RNA Bases	C	U	A	G
DNA Bases				

Observation: RNA Structure

1. If you are using a kit, draw a nucleotide for the construction of mRNA. *Label the ribose (the sugar in RNA), the phosphate, and the base in your drawing and in 1–3, Figure 11.3.*

2. Complete Table 11.4 by writing in the colors of the bases for Figure 11.3 and for your kit.

Table 11.4 Base Colors		
	In Figure 11.3	**In Your Kit**
Cytosine		
Uracil		
Adenine		
Guanine		

3. The base uracil substitutes for the base thymine in RNA. Complete Table 11.5 to show the several other ways RNA differs from DNA.

Table 11.5 DNA Structure Compared with RNA Structure		
	DNA	**RNA**
Sugar	Deoxyribose	
Bases	Adenine, guanine, thymine, cytosine	
Strands	Double stranded with base pairing	
Helix	Yes	

11.3 DNA and Protein Synthesis

Protein synthesis requires the processes of transcription and translation. During **transcription,** which takes place in the nucleus, an RNA molecule called **messenger RNA (mRNA)** is made complementary to one of the DNA strands. This mRNA leaves the nucleus and goes to the ribosomes in the cytoplasm. Ribosomes are composed of **ribosomal RNA (rRNA)** and proteins in two subunits.

During **translation,** RNA molecules called **transfer RNA (tRNA)** bring amino acids to the ribosome, and they join in the order prescribed by mRNA. This sequence of amino acids was originally specified by DNA. This is the information that DNA, the genetic material, stores. Explain the role DNA, mRNA, and tRNA have in protein synthesis here:_____

_____

Transcription

During transcription, complementary RNA is made from a DNA template (Fig. 11.4). A portion of DNA unwinds and unzips at the point of attachment of the enzyme RNA polymerase. A strand of mRNA is produced when complementary nucleotides join in the order dictated by the sequence of bases in DNA. Transcription occurs in the nucleus, and the mRNA passes out of the nucleus to enter the cytoplasm.

Label Figure 11.4. For number 1, note the name of the enzyme that carries out mRNA synthesis. For number 2, note the name of this molecule.

Observation: Transcription

1. If you are using a kit, unzip your DNA model so that only one strand remains. This strand is the **sense strand,** the strand that is transcribed.
2. Using Figure 11.4 as a guide, construct a messenger RNA (mRNA) molecule by first lining up RNA nucleotides complementary to the sense strand of your DNA molecule. Join the nucleotides together to form mRNA.
3. A portion of DNA has the sequence of bases shown in Table 11.6. *Complete Table 11.6 to show the sequence of bases in mRNA.*
4. If you are using a kit, unzip mRNA transcript from the DNA. Locate the end of the strand that will move to the _____ in the cytoplasm.

Figure 11.4 Messenger RNA (mRNA).
Messenger RNA complementary to a section of DNA forms during transcription.

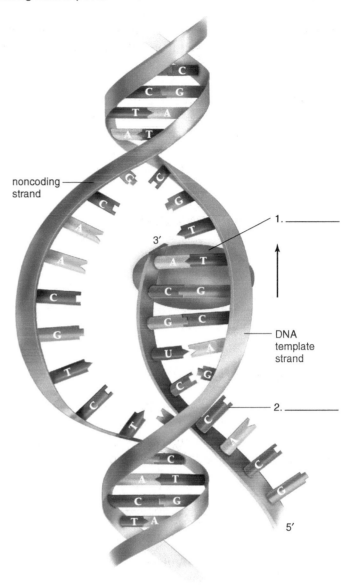

noncoding strand

3′

1. _____

DNA template strand

2. _____

5′

Table 11.6	Transcription																	
DNA	T	A	C	A	C	G	A	G	C	A	A	C	T	A	A	C	A	T
mRNA																		

Translation

DNA specifies the sequence of amino acids in a polypeptide because every three bases stand for an amino acid. Therefore, DNA is said to have a **triplet code.** The bases in mRNA are complementary to the bases in DNA. Every three bases in mRNA are called a **codon.** One codon of mRNA represents one amino acid. Thus, the sequence of DNA bases serves as the blueprint for the sequence of amino acids assembled to make a protein. The correct sequence of amino acids in a polypeptide is the message that mRNA carries.

Messenger RNA leaves the nucleus and proceeds to the ribosomes, where protein synthesis occurs. Transfer RNA (tRNA) molecules are so named because they transfer amino acids to the ribosomes. Each RNA has a specific tRNA amino acid at one end and a matching **anticodon** at the other end (Fig. 11.5). *Label Figure 11.5,* where the amino acid is represented as a colored ball, the tRNA is green, and the anticodon is the sequence of three bases. (The anticodon is complementary to the mRNA codon.)

Figure 11.5 Transfer RNA (tRNA).
Transfer RNA carries amino acids to the ribosomes.

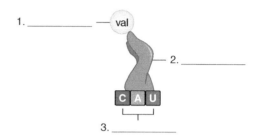

Observation: Translation

1. Figure 11.6 shows seven tRNA–amino acid complexes. Every amino acid has a name; in the figure, only the first three letters of the name are inside the ball. Using the mRNA sequence given in Table 11.7, number the tRNA–amino acid complexes in the order they will come to the ribosome.
2. If you are using a kit, arrange your tRNA–amino acid complexes in the order consistent with Table 11.7. Complete Table 11.7. Why are the codons and anticodons in groups of three? _____

_____

Figure 11.6 Transfer RNA diversity.
Each type of tRNA carries only one particular amino acid, designated here by the first three letters of its name.

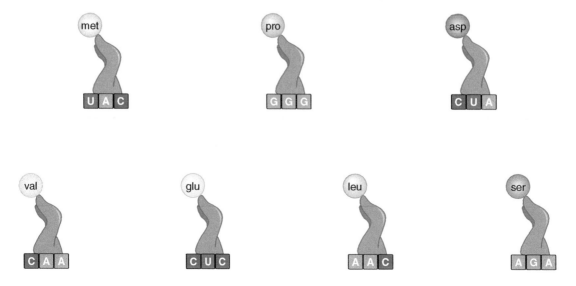

Table 11.7 Translation

mRNA codons	AUG	CCC	GAG	GUU	GAU	UUG	UCU
tRNA anticodons							
Amino acid*							

*Use three letters only. See Table 11.8 for the full names of these amino acids.

Table 11.8 Names of Amino Acids

Abbreviation	Name
met	methionine
pro	proline
asp	aspartate
val	valine
glu	glutamate
leu	leucine
ser	serine

3. Figure 11.7 shows the manner in which the polypeptide grows. A ribosome has three binding sites. They are the A (amino acid) site, the P (peptide) site, and the E (exit) site. A tRNA leaves from the E site after it has passed its amino acid or peptide to the newly arrived tRNA–amino acid complex. Then the ribosome moves forward, making room for the next tRNA–amino acid. This sequence of events occurs over and over until the entire polypeptide is borne by the last tRNA to come to the ribosome. Then a release factor releases the polypeptide chain from the ribosome. *In Figure 11.7, label the ribosome, the mRNA, and the peptide. Also, indicate the A, P, and E sites.*

Figure 11.7 Protein synthesis.

1. A ribosome has a site for two tRNA–amino acid complexes. 2. Before a tRNA leaves, an RNA passes its attached peptide to newly arrived tRNA–amino acid complex. 3. The ribosome moves forward, and the next tRNA–amino acid complex arrives.

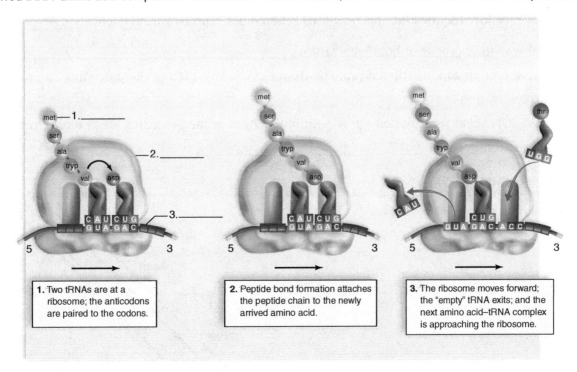

1. Two tRNAs are at a ribosome; the anticodons are paired to the codons.

2. Peptide bond formation attaches the peptide chain to the newly arrived amino acid.

3. The ribosome moves forward; the "empty" tRNA exits; and the next amino acid–tRNA complex is approaching the ribosome.

11.4   Isolation of DNA

In the following Experimental Procedure, you will isolate DNA from the cells of an organism using a modified procedure like that used worldwide in biotechnology laboratories. You will extract DNA from a vegetable or fruit filtrate that contains DNA in solution. To prepare the filtrate, your instructor homogenized the vegetable or fruit with a detergent. The detergent emulsifies and forms complexes with the lipids and proteins of the plasma membrane, causing them to precipitate out of solution. Cell contents, including DNA, become suspended in solution. The cellular mixture is then filtered to produce the filtrate that contains DNA and its adhering proteins.

The DNA molecule is easily degraded (broken down), so it is important to closely follow all instructions. Handle glassware carefully to prevent nucleases in your skin from contaminating the glassware.

Experimental Procedure: Isolating DNA

1. Obtain a pair of gloves and wear them when doing this procedure.
2. Obtain a large, clean test tube, and place it in an ice bath. Let stand for a few minutes to make sure the test tube is cold. Everything must be kept very cold.
3. Obtain approximately 4 ml of the *filtrate*, and add it to your test tube while keeping the tube in the ice bath.
4. Obtain and add 2 ml of cold *meat tenderizer solution* to the solution in the test tube, and mix the contents slightly with a stirring rod or Pasteur pipette. Let stand for 10 minutes so the enzyme has time to strip the DNA of protein.
5. Use a graduated cylinder or pipette to slowly add an equal volume (approximately 6 ml) of ice-cold *95% ethanol* along the inside of the test tube. Keep the tube in the ice bath, and tilt it to a 45° angle. You should see a distinct layer of ethanol over the white precipitate, the DNA. Let the tube sit for 2 to 3 minutes.
6. Insert a glass rod or a Pasteur pipette into the tube until it reaches the bottom of the tube. *Gently* swirl the glass rod or pipette, always in the same direction. (You are not trying to mix the two layers; you are trying to wind the DNA onto the glass rod like cotton candy.) This process is called "spooling" the DNA. The stringy, slightly gelatinous material that attaches to the pipette is DNA (Fig. 11.8). If the DNA has been damaged, it will still precipitate, but as white flakes that cannot be collected on the glass rod.
7. Answer the following questions:

   a. This procedure requires homogenization. When did homogenization occur? _____

      What was the purpose of homogenization? _____

   b. Next, deproteinization stripped proteins from the DNA. Which of the preceding steps represents deproteinization? _____

   c. Finally, DNA was precipitated out of solution. Which of the preceding steps represents the precipitation of DNA? _____

Figure 11.8   Isolation of DNA.
The addition of ethanol causes DNA to come out of solution so that it can be spooled onto a glass rod.

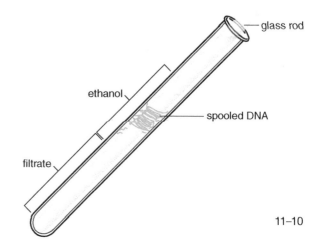

glass rod

ethanol

spooled DNA

filtrate

11.5 Genetic Disorders

The base sequence of DNA in all the chromosomes is an organism's genome. Now that the Human Genome Project is finished, we know the normal order of all the 3.6 billion nucleotide bases in the human genome. Someday it will be possible to sequence anyone's genome within a relatively short time, and thereby determine what particular base sequence alterations signify that he or she has a disorder or will have one in the future. In this laboratory, you will study the alteration in base sequence that causes a person to have sickle-cell disease.

In persons with sickle-cell disease, the red blood cells aren't biconcave disks like normal red blood cells—they are sickle shaped. Sickle-shaped cells can't pass along narrow capillary passage-ways. They clog the vessels and break down, causing the person to suffer from poor circulation, anemia, and poor resistance to infection. Internal hemorrhaging leads to further complications, such as jaundice, episodic pain in the abdomen and joints, and damage to internal organs.

Sickle-shaped red blood cells are caused by an abnormal hemoglobin (Hb^S). Individuals with the Hb^AHb^A genotype are normal; those with the Hb^SHb^S genotype have sickle-cell disease, and those with the Hb^AHb^S have sickle-cell trait. Persons with sickle-cell trait do not usually have sickle-shaped cells unless they experience dehydration or mild oxygen deprivation.

Genomic Sequence for Sickle-Cell Disease

Examine Figures 11.9a and b, which show the DNA base sequence, the mRNA codons, and the amino acid sequence for a portion of Hb^A and the same portion for Hb^S.

Figure 11.9 Sickle-cell disease.
a. When red blood cells are normal, the base sequence (in one location) for Hb^A alleles is CTC. **b.** In sickle-cell disease at these locations, it is CAC.

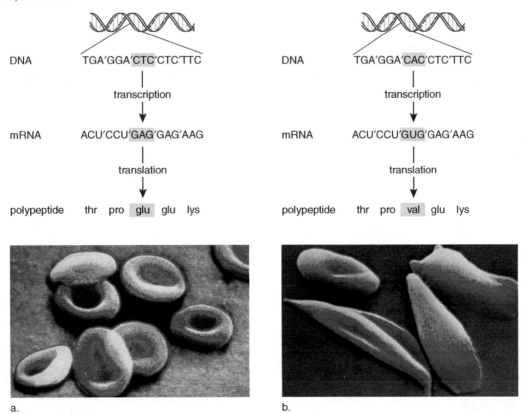

1. In what three-DNA-base sequence does *Hb*^{A} differ from *Hb*^{S}?   *Hb*^{A} _____   *Hb*^{S} _____

2. What are the codons for these three bases?   *Hb*^{A} _____   *Hb*^{S} _____

3. What is the amino acid difference?   *Hb*^{A} _____   *Hb*^{S} _____

This one amino acid difference causes the polypeptide chain in sickle-cell hemoglobin to pile up as firm rods that push against the plasma membrane and deform the red blood cell into a sickle shape:

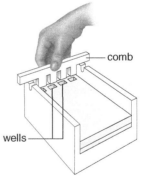

Gel Electrophoresis

The two most widely used techniques for separating molecules in biotechnology are chromatography and gel electrophoresis. Chromatography separates molecules on the basis of their solubility and size. **Gel electrophoresis** separates molecules on the basis of their charge and size (Fig. 11.10).

During gel electrophoresis, charged molecules migrate across a span of gel (gelatinous slab) because they are placed in a powerful electrical field. In the present experiment, the fragment mixture for each DNA sample is placed in a small depression in the gel called a well. The gel is placed in a powerful electrical field. The electricity causes equal length DNA fragments, which are negatively charged, to move through the gel to the positive pole at a faster rate than those that have no charge.

Almost all gel electrophoresis is carried out using horizontal gel slabs. First, the gel is poured onto a glass plate, and the wells are formed. After the samples are added to the wells, the gel and the glass plate are put into an electrophoresis chamber, and buffer is added. The fragments begin to migrate after the electrical current is turned on. With staining, the fragments appear as a series of bands spread from one end of the gel to the other.

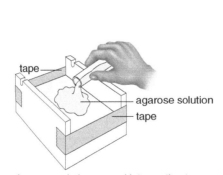

a. Agarose solution poured into casting tray

b. Comb that forms wells for samples

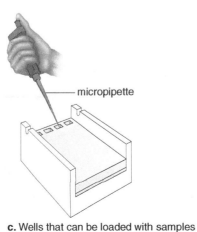

c. Wells that can be loaded with samples

d. Electrophoresis chamber and power supply

Figure 11.10   Equipment and procedure for gel electrophoresis.

In this procedure, you will perform gel electrophoresis, if instructed to do so, and analyze your data to come to a conclusion.

Performing Gel Electrophoresis

1. Obtain three samples of hemoglobin provided by your kit. They are labeled sample A, B, and C.
2. If so directed by your instructor, carry out gel electrophoresis of these samples (see Fig. 11.10).

> ⚠ **Gel electrophoresis** Students should wear personal protective equipment: safety goggles and smocks or aprons while loading gels and during electrophoresis and protective gloves while staining.

Analyzing the Electrophoresed Gel

1. Sickle-cell hemoglobin (Hb^S) migrates slower toward the positive pole than normal hemoglobin (Hb^A) because the amino acid valine has no polar R groups, whereas the amino acid glutamate does have a polar R group.
2. In Figure 11.11, label the lane that contains only Hb^S, signifying that the individual is Hb^SHb^S.
3. Label the lane that contains only Hb^A, signifying that the individual is Hb^AHb^A.
4. Label the lane that contains both Hb^S and Hb^A, signifying that the individual is Hb^AHb^S.

Figure 11.11   Gel electrophoresis of hemoglobins.

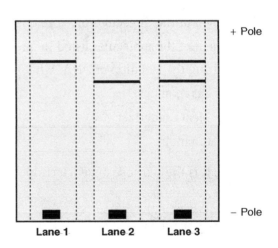

Conclusion: Genomic Sequence for Sickle-Cell Disease

- You are a genetic counselor. A young couple seeks your advice because sickle-cell disease occurs among the family members of each. You order DNA base sequencing to be done. The results come back that at one of the two loci for normal Hb^A, each has the abnormal sequence CAC instead of CTC. The other locus is normal. What genotype do they each have? _____ What are the chances that this couple will have a child with sickle-cell disease (Hb^A is dominant and Hb^S is recessive)? _____

Laboratory Review 11

1. Explain why DNA is said to have a structure that resembles a ladder.

2. How is complementary base pairing different when pairing DNA to DNA than when pairing DNA to mRNA?

3. Explain why the genetic code is called a triplet code.

4. What role does each of the following molecules play in protein synthesis?

   a. DNA

   b. mRNA

   c. tRNA

   d. Amino acids

5. Which of the molecules listed in question 4 are involved in transcription?

6. Which of the molecules listed in question 4 are involved in translation?

7. During the isolation of DNA, what role was played by these substances?

   a. Detergent

   b. Meat tenderizer

   c. Ethanol

8. What is the purpose of gel electrophoresis?

9. Why does sickle-cell hemoglobin (Hb^S) migrate slower than normal hemoglobin (Hb^A) during gel electrophoresis?

10. Why are red blood cells sickle shaped in a person with sickle-cell disease?

12

Evidences of Evolution

Learning Outcomes

Introduction

Evolution is the process by which life has changed through time. A **species** is a group of similarly constructed organisms that share common genes, and a **population** is all the members of a species living in a particular area. When new variations arise that allow certain members of a population to capture more resources, these individuals tend to survive and to have more offspring than the other, unchanged members. Therefore, each successive generation will include more members with the new variation. Eventually, most members of a population and then the species will have the same **adaptations,** structures, physiology, and behavior that make an organism suited to its environment.

Adaptations to various ways of life explain why life is so diverse. However, evolution, which has been ongoing since the origin of life, is also an explanation for the unity of life. All organisms share the same characteristics of life because they can trace their ancestry to the first cell or cells. Many different lines of evidence support this hypothesis of common descent, and the more varied the evidence supporting the hypothesis, the more certain the hypothesis becomes.

In this laboratory, you will study three types of data that support the hypothesis of common descent: (1) the fossil record, (2) comparative anatomy (embryological and adult), and (3) molecular differences. **Fossils** are the remains or evidence of some organism that lived long ago. Fossils can be used to trace the history of life on Earth. A comparative study of the anatomy of modern groups of organisms has shown that each group has structures of similar construction called **homologous structures.** For example, all vertebrate animals have essentially the same type of skeleton. Homologous structures signify relatedness through evolution. Living organisms use the same basic molecules including ATP, the carrier of energy in cells; DNA, which makes up genes; and proteins, such as enzymes and antibodies. In this laboratory, you will use an antigen-antibody reaction to show the degree of evolutionary relatedness between different vertebrates.

Table 12.1 The Geological Timescale: Major Divisions of Geological Time and some of the Major Evolutionary Events that Occurred

Era	Period	Epoch	Millions of Years Ago	Plant Life	Animal Life
Cenozoic*	Quaternary	Holocene	0.01–present	Human influence on plant life.	Age of Homo sapiens.
				Significant Mammalian Extinction	
		Pleistocene	1.8–0.01	Herbaceous plants spread and diversify	Presence of ice age mammals. Modern humans appear.
	Tertiary	Pliocene	5.3–1.8	Herbaceous angiosperms flourish.	First hominids appear.
		Miocene	23–5.3	Grasslands spread as forests contract.	Apelike mammals and grazing mammals flourish; insects flourish.
		Oligocene	33.9–23	Many modern families of flowering plants evolve.	Browsing mammals and monkeylike primates appear.
		Eocene	55.8–33.9	Subtropical forests with heavy rainfall thrive.	All modern orders of mammals are represented.
		Paleocene	65.5–55.8	Flowering plants continue to diversify	Primitive primates, herbivores, carnivores, and insectivores appear.
				Mass Extinction: Dinosaurs and Most Reptiles	
Mesozoic	Cretaceous		145.5–65.5	Flowering plants, conifers persist.	Placental mammals appear; modern insect groups appear.
	Jurassic		199.6–145.5	Flowering plants appear	Dinosaurs flourish; birds appear.
				Mass Extinction	
	Triassic		251–199.6	Forests of conifers and cycads dominate.	First mammals appear; first dinosaurs appear; corals and molluscs dominate seas.
				Mass Extinction	
Paleozoic	Permian		299–251	Gymnosperms diversify.	Reptiles diversify; amphibians decline.
	Carboniferous		359.2–299	Age of great coal-forming forests: Ferns, club mosses, and horsetails flourish.	Amphibians diversify; first reptiles appear; first great radiation of insects.
				Mass Extinction	
	Devonian		416–359.2	First seed plants appear. Seedless vascular plants diversify.	Jawed fishes diversify and dominate the seas; first insects and first amphibians appear.
	Silurian		443.7–416	Seedless vascular plants appear.	First jawed fishes appear.
				Mass Extinction	
	Ordovician		488.3–443.7	Nonvascular land plants appear Marine algae flourish.	Invertebrates spread and diversify; jawless fishes (first vertebrates) appear.
	Cambrian		542–488.3	First plants appear on land. Marine algae flourish.	All invertebrate phyla present; first chordates appear.
Precambrian Time			600	Oldest soft-bodied invertebrate fossils	
			1,400–700	Protists evolve and diversify	
			2,200	Oldest eukaryotic fossils.	
			2,700	O_2 accumulates in atmosphere.	
			3,500	Oldest known fossils (prokaryotes)	
			4,600	Earth forms.	

*Many authorities divide the Cenozoic era into the Paleogene period (contains the Paleocene. Eocene, and Oligocene epochs) and the Neogene period (contains the Miocene, Pliocene, Pleistocene, and Holocene epochs).

12.1 Evidence from the Fossil Record

Because all life-forms evolved from the first cell or cells, life has a history, and this history is revealed by the fossil record. The geologic timescale, which was developed by both geologists and paleontologists, depicts the history of life based on the fossil record (Table 12.1). In this section, we will study the geologic timescale and then examine some fossils.

Geologic Timescale

Divisions of the Timescale

Notice that the timescale divides the history of Earth into eras, then periods, and then epochs. The three eras span the greatest amounts of time, and the epochs are the shortest time frames. Notice that only the periods of the Cenozoic era are divided into epochs, meaning that more attention is given to the evolution of primates and flowering plants than to the earlier evolving organisms. Modern civilization is given its own epoch, despite the fact that humans have only been around about .04% of the history of life. List the four eras in the timescale starting with Precambrian time: _____

How to Read the Timescale

1. Using the geologic timescale, you can trace the history of life by beginning with Precambrian time at the bottom of the timescale. The timescale indicates that the first cells (the prokaryotes) arose some 3,500 MYA. The prokaryotes evolved before any other group. Why do you read the timescale starting at the bottom? _____

2. The Precambrian time was very long, lasting from the time the Earth first formed until 542 MYA. The fossil record during the Precambrian time is meager, but the fossil record from the Cambrian period onward is rich (for reasons still being determined). This helps explain why the timescale usually does not show any periods until the Cambrian period of the Paleozoic era. You can also use the timescale to check when certain groups evolved and/or flourished.
   Example: During the Ordovician period, the nonvascular plants appear on land, and the first jawless and jawed fishes appear in the seas.

   During the _____ era and the _____ period, the first flowering plants appear. How many million years ago was this? _____

3. On the timescale, note the Carboniferous period. During this period great swamp forests covered the land. These are also called coal-forming forests because, with time, they became the coal we burn today. How do you know that the plants in this forest were not flowering trees, as most of our trees are today? _____ What type animal was diversifying at this time?

4. You should associate the Cenozoic era with the evolution of humans. Among mammals, humans are primates. During what period and epoch did primates appear? _____
   Among primates, humans are hominins. During what period and epoch did hominins appear?
   _____ The scientific name for humans is *Homo sapiens*.
   What period and epoch is the age of *Homo sapiens*? _____

Dating Within the Timescale

The timescale provides both relative dates and absolute dates. When you say, for example, "Flowering plants evolved during the Jurassic period," you are using relative time, because flowering plants evolved earlier or later than groups in other periods. If you use the dates that are given in millions of years (MYA), you are using absolute time. Absolute dates are usually obtained by measuring the amount of a radioactive isotope in the rocks surrounding the fossils. Why wouldn't you expect to find human fossils and dinosaur fossils together in rocks dated similarly? _____

Limitations of the Timescale

Because the timescale tells when various groups evolved and flourished, it might seem that evolution has been a series of events leading only from the first cells to humans. This is not the case; for example, prokaryotes (bacteria and archaea) never declined and are still the most abundant and successful organisms on Earth. Even today, they constitute up to 90% of the total weight of living things.

Then, too, the timescale lists mass extinctions, but it doesn't tell when specific groups became extinct. **Extinction** is the total disappearance of a species or a higher group; **mass extinction** occurs when a large number of species disappear in a few million years or less. For lack of space, the geologic timescale can't depict in detail what happened to the members of every group mentioned. Figure 12.1 does show how mass extinction affected a few groups of animals. Which of the animals shown in

Figure 12.1 suffered the most during the P-T (Permain-Triassic) extinction? _____
The K-T extinction occurred between the Cretaceous and the Tertiary periods. Which animals shown in

Figure 12.1 became extinct during the K-T extinction? _____
Figure 12.1 shows only periods and no eras. Fill in the eras on the lines provided in the figure.

Figure 12.1   Mass extinctions.
Five significant mass extinctions and their effects on the abundance of certain forms of marine and terrestrial life. The width of the horizontal bars indicates the varying abundance of each life-form considered.

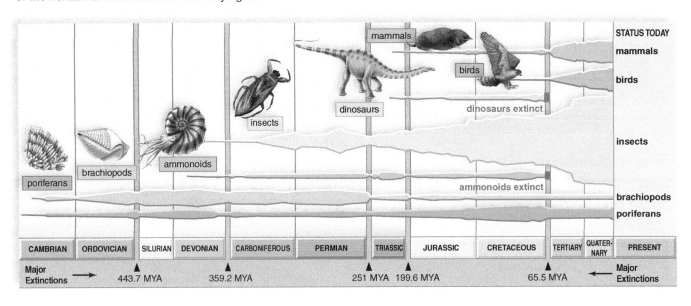

Observation: Fossils

1. Obtain a box of selected fossils. If the fossils are embedded in rocks, examine the rock until you have found the fossil. Fossils are embedded in rocks because the sediment that originally surrounded them hardened over time. Most fossils consist of hard parts such as shells, bones, or teeth because these parts are not consumed or decomposed over time. One possible reason the Cambrian might be rich in fossils is that organisms before this time did not have

_____.

2. The kit you are using, or your instructor, will identify which of the fossils are invertebrate animals. These fossils date back to which era and period? _____ Fill in the title of Table 12.2. List the names of these fossils in Table 12.2 and give a description of the fossil part that survived.

Table 12.2 Invertebrate Fossils from the _____ Era _____ Period	
Type of Fossil	Description of Hard Part

3. Which of the fossils available to you are vertebrates? _____
Use Table 12.1 to associate each fossil with the particular era and period when this type animal was most abundant. Fill in Table 12.3 according to sequence of the time frames from the latest (*top*) to earliest (*bottom*).

Table 12.3 Vertebrate Fossils		
Type of Fossil	Era, Period	Description of Hard Part

4. Which of the fossils available to you are plants? _____ Plants that have no hard parts become fossils when their impressions are filled in by minerals. Use Table 12.1 to associate each plant with a particular era and period. Assume trees are flowering plants and associate them with the era and period when flowering plants were most abundant. Fill in Table 12.4 according to the sequence of the time frames from the latest (*top*) to earliest (*bottom*).

Table 12.4 Plant Fossils		
Type of Fossil	Era; Period	Description of Fossil

12.2 Evidence from Comparative Anatomy

In the study of evolutionary relationships, organisms or parts of organisms are said to be **homologous** if they exhibit similar basic structures and embryonic origins. If these organisms or parts of organisms are similar in function only, they are said to be **analogous.** Only homologous structures indicate an evolutionary relationship and are used to classify organisms.

Comparison of Adult Vertebrate Forelimbs

The limbs of vertebrates are homologous structures. Homologous structures share a basic pattern, although there may be specific differences. The similarity of homologous structures is explainable by descent from a common ancestor.

Observation: Vertebrate Forelimbs

1. The central diagram in Figure 12.2 represents the forelimb bones of the ancestral vertebrate. The basic components are the humerus (h), ulna (u), radius (r), carpals (c), metacarpals (m), and phalanges (p) in the five digits.
2. Carefully compare and label in Figure 12.2 the corresponding forelimb bones of the frog, the lizard, the bird, the bat, the cat, and the human. In particular, note the specific modifications that have occurred in some of the bones to meet the demands of a particular way of life.
3. Fill in Table 12.5 to indicate which bones in each specimen appear to most resemble the ancestral condition and which most differ from the ancestral condition.
4. Relate the change in bone structure to mode of locomotion in two examples.

   Example 1: _____

   Example 2: _____

Table 12.5 Comparison of Vertebrate Forelimbs		
Animal	**Bones That Resemble Common Ancestor**	**Bones That Differ from Common Ancestor**
Frog		
Lizard		
Bird		
Bat		
Cat		
Human		

Conclusion: Vertebrate Forelimbs

- Vertebrates are descended from a _____, but they are adapted

  to _____.

Figure 12.2 Vertebrate forelimbs.

Because all vertebrates evolved from a common ancestor, their forelimbs share homologous structures.

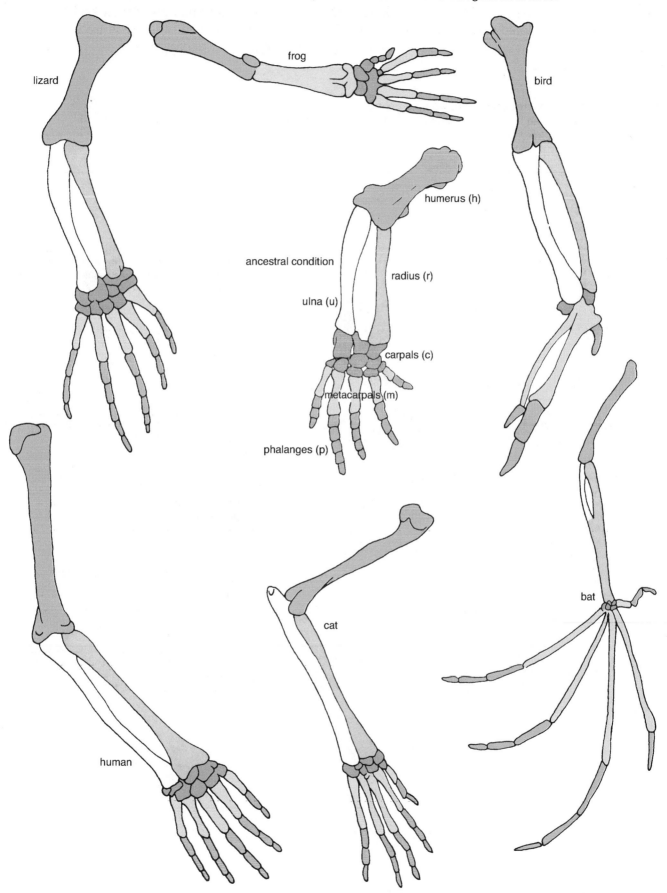

Comparison of Chimpanzee and Human Skeletons

Chimpanzees and humans are closely related, as is apparent from an examination of their skeletons. However, they are adapted to different ways of life. Chimpanzees are adapted to living in trees and are herbivores—they eat mainly plants. Humans are adapted to walking on the ground and are omnivores—they eat both plants and meat.

Figure 12.3 Human and chimpanzee skeletons.
Differences in posture can be related to their adaptations to a different habitat. Humans now walk on land and chimpanzees primarily live in trees.

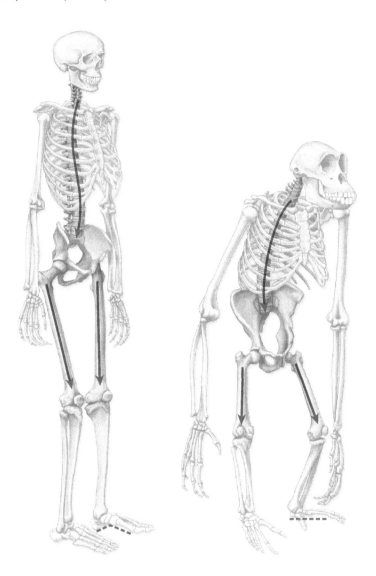

Human spine exits from the skull's center; ape spine exits from rear of skull.

Human spine is S-shaped; ape spine has a slight curve.

Human pelvis is bowl-shaped; ape pelvis is longer and more narrow.

Human femurs angle inward to the knees; ape femurs angle out a bit.

Human knee can support more weight than ape knee.

Human foot has an arch; ape foot has no arch.

Observation: Chimpanzee and Human Skeletons

Posture

Chimpanzees are arboreal and climb in trees. While on the ground, they tend to knuckle-walk, with their hands bent. Humans are terrestrial and walk erect. Compare the posture of a chimpanzee and human (Fig. 12.3) by answering the following questions:

1. **Head and torso:** Where are the head and trunk with relation to the hips and legs—thrust forward over the hips and legs or balanced over the hips and legs? *Record your observations in Table 12.6.*

2. **Spine:** Which animal has a long and curved lumbar region, and which has a short and stiff lumbar region? *Record your observations in Table 12.6.*

   How does this contribute to an erect posture in humans? _____

   _____

3. **Pelvis:** Chimpanzees sway when they walk because lifting one leg throws them off balance. Which animal has a narrow and long pelvis, and which has a broad and short pelvis? *Record your observations in Table 12.6.*

4. **Femur:** In humans, the femur better supports the trunk. In which animal is the femur angled between articulations with the pelvic girdle and the knee? In which animal is the femur straight with no angle? *Record your observations in Table 12.6.*

5. **Knee joint:** In humans, the knee joint is modified to support the body's weight. In which animal is the femur larger at the bottom and the tibia larger at the top? *Record your observations in Table 12.6.*

6. **Foot:** In humans, the foot is adapted for walking long distances and running with less chance of injury.

   In which animal is the big toe opposable? _____ How does an opposable toe assist

   chimpanzees? _____

   Which foot has an arch? _____ How does an arch assist humans? _____
   Record your observations in Table 12.6.

7. How does the difference in the position of the foramen magnum, a large opening in the base of the skull for the spinal cord, correlate with the posture and stance of the two organisms?

   _____

Table 12.6 Comparison of Chimpanzee and Human Postures

Skeletal Part	Chimpanzee	Human
1. Head and torso		
2. Spine		
3. Pelvis		
4. Femur		
5. Knee joint		
6. Foot: Opposable toe		
Arch		

Conclusion: Chimpanzee and Human Skeletons

- Do your observations show that the skeletal differences between chimpanzees and humans can be related to posture? _____ Explain. _____

Figure 12.4 Chimpanzee and human skulls.
Differences in facial features can be related to a difference in diet. Chimpanzees are herbivorous, and humans are omnivores.

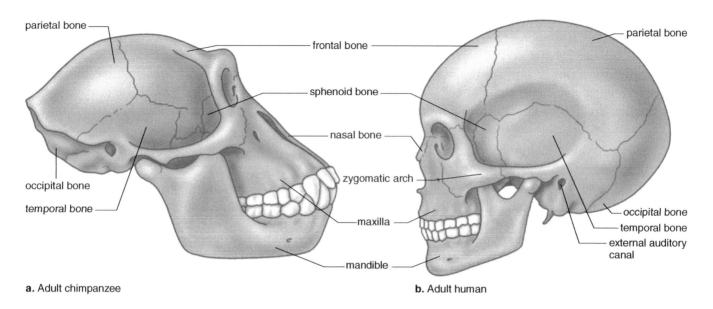

a. Adult chimpanzee   **b.** Adult human

Facial Features

Humans are omnivorous. A diet rich in meat does not require strong grinding teeth or well-developed facial muscles. Chimpanzees are herbivores, and a vegetarian diet requires strong teeth and strong facial muscles that attach to bony projections. Compare the skulls of the chimpanzee and the human in Figure 12.4 and answer the following questions:

1. **Supraorbital ridge:** For which skull is the supraorbital ridge (the region of frontal bone just above the eye socket) thicker? *Record your observations in Table 12.7.*
2. **Frontal bone:** Compare the slope of the frontal bones of the chimpanzee and human skulls. How are they different? *Record your observations in Table 12.7.*
3. **Teeth:** Examine the teeth in the adult chimpanzee and adult human skulls. Are the shapes and size of teeth similar in both? *Record your observations in Table 12.7.*
4. **Chin:** What is the position of the mouth and chin in relation to the profile for each skull? *Record your observations in Table 12.7.*

Table 12.7 Facial Features of Chimpanzees and Humans		
Feature	**Chimpanzee**	**Human**
1. Supraorbital ridge		
2. Slope of frontal bone		
3. Teeth		
4. Chin		

Conclusion: Facial Features

- Do your observations show that diet can be related to the facial features of chimpanzees and humans? _____ Explain. _____

Comparison of Vertebrate Embryos

The anatomy shared by vertebrates extends to their embryological development. For example, as embryos, they all have a postanal tail, somites (segmented blocks of mesoderm lying on either side of the notochord), and paired pharyngeal pouches. In aquatic animals, these pouches become functional gills (Fig. 12.5). In humans, the first pair of pouches becomes the cavity of the middle ear and auditory tube, the second pair becomes the tonsils, and the third and fourth pairs become the thymus and parathyroid glands.

Figure 12.5 Vertebrate embryos.
During early developmental stages, vertebrate embryos have certain characteristics in common.

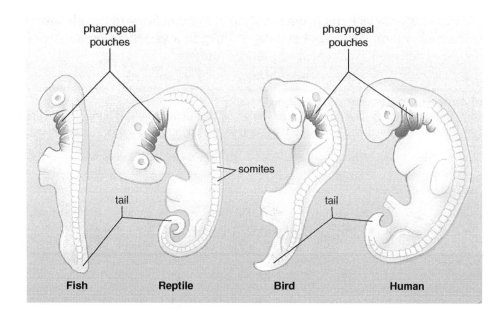

Observation: Chick and Pig Embryos

1. Obtain prepared slides of vertebrate embryos at comparable stages of development. Observe each of the embryos using a stereomicroscope.
2. List five similarities of the embryos:

    a. _____

    b. _____

    c. _____

    d. _____

    e. _____

Conclusion: Vertebrate Embryos

- Vertebrate embryos resemble one another because _____

    _____.

12.3 Molecular Evidence

Almost all living organisms use the same basic biochemical molecules, including DNA, ATP, and many identical and nearly identical enzymes. In addition, living organisms utilize the same DNA triplet code and the same 20 amino acids in their proteins. There is no obvious functional reason these elements need to be so similar. Therefore, their similarity is best explained by descent from a common ancestor.

Protein Differences

According to the **protein clock hypothesis,** the number of amino acid changes between organisms is proportional to the length of time since two organisms began evolving separately from a common

ancestor. Why should that be? _____

The sequence of amino acids in **cytochrome c,** a carrier of electrons in the electron transport chain found in mitochondria and chloroplasts, has been determined in a variety of organisms. Figure 12.6 lists the number of differences between amino acid sequences for several of these.

Figure 12.6   Significance of molecular differences.

The branch points in this diagram indicate the number of amino acids that differ between human cytochrome c and the organisms depicted. These molecular data are consistent with those provided by a study of the fossil record and comparative anatomy.

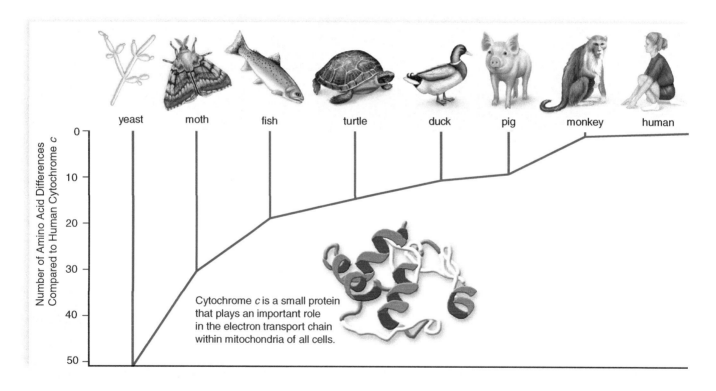

Protein Similarities

The immune system makes **antibodies** (proteins) that react with foreign proteins, termed **antigens.** Antigen-antibody reactions are specific. An antibody will react only with a particular antigen. In today's laboratory, this reaction can be observed when a precipitate, a substance separated from the solution, appears.

Figure 12.7 Antigen-antibody reaction.
When antibodies react to antigens, a complex forms that appears as a precipitate.

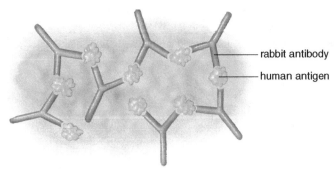

Antigen-Antibody Complex

Experimental Procedure: Protein Similarities

In this procedure, it is assumed that human serum (containing human antigens) is injected into the bloodstream of a rabbit, and the rabbit makes antibodies against human antigens (Fig. 12.7). The experiment tests this sensitized rabbit serum against the antigens of other animals. The stronger the reaction (determined by the amount of precipitate), the more closely related the animal is to humans.

1. Obtain a chemplate (a clear glass tray with wells), one bottle of synthetic *human blood serum,* one bottle of synthetic *rabbit blood serum,* and five bottles (I–V) of *blood serum test solution.*
2. Put two drops of synthetic rabbit blood serum in each of the six wells in the chemplate. Label the wells 1–6. See yellow circles in Figure 12.8.
3. Add 2 drops of synthetic human blood serum to each well. See red circles in Figure 12.8. Stir with the plastic stirring rod that was attached to the chemplate. The rabbit serum has now been "sensitized" to human serum. (This simulates the production of antibodies in the rabbit's bloodstream in response to the human blood proteins.)
4. Rinse the stirrer. (The large cavity of the chemplate may be filled with water to facilitate rinsing.)
5. Add 4 drops of *blood serum test solution III* (tests for human blood proteins) to well 6.

   Describe what you see. _____

   _____

   This well will serve as the basis by which to compare all the other samples of test blood serum.
6. Now add 4 drops of *blood serum test solution I* to well 1. Stir and observe. Rinse the stirrer. Do the same for each of the remaining *blood serum test solutions (II–V)*—adding II to well 2, III to well 3, and so on. Be sure to rinse the stirrer after each use.
7. At the end of 10 and 20 minutes, record the amount of precipitate in each of the six wells in Figure 12.8. Well 6 is recorded as having $++++$ amount of precipitate after both 10 and 20 minutes. Compare the other wells with this well ($+$ = trace amount; 0 = none). Holding the plate slightly above your head at arm's length and looking at the underside toward an overhead light source will allow you to more clearly determine the amount of precipitate.

Figure 12.8 Molecular evidence of evolution.
The greater the amount of precipitate, the more closely related an animal is to humans.

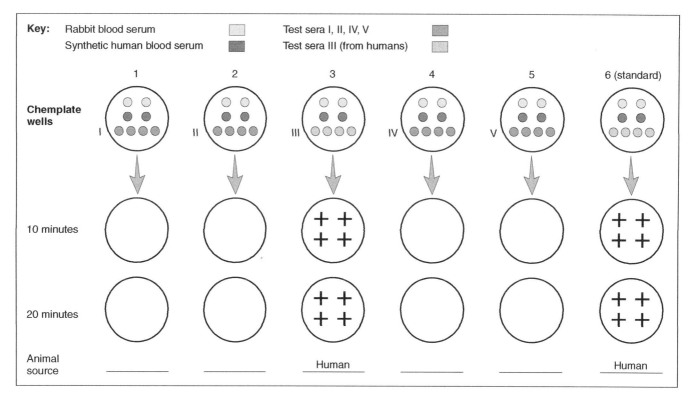

Conclusions: Protein Similarities

- The last row in Figure 12.8 tells you that the test serum in well 3 is from a human. How do your test results confirm this? _____
- Aside from humans, the test sera (supposedly) came from a pig, a monkey, an orangutan, and a chimpanzee. Which is most closely related to humans—the pig or the chimpanzee?

  _____

- Judging by the amount of precipitate, complete the last row in Figure 12.8 by indicating which serum you believe came from which animal. On what do you base your conclusions?

  _____

  _____

- In Section 12.2, a comparison of bones in vertebrate forelimbs showed that vertebrates share a common ancestor. Molecular evidence shows us that of the vertebrates studied, _____ and _____, are most closely related. In evolution, closely related organisms share a recent common ancestor. Humans share a more recent common ancestor with chimpanzees than they do with pigs.

12.4   Summarizing the Evidences of Evolution

Work with a partner or in a group to conclude that your observations in this laboratory give evidences of evolution.

Evidence from the Fossil Record

In this section, you studied the geologic timescale (p. 148). The geologic timescale gives powerful evidence of evolution because:

1. Fossils are _____.

2. Fossils can be arranged in a sequential manner because _____.

3. Younger fossils and not older fossils are more like _____.

4. In short, the fossil record shows _____.

Evidence from Comparative Anatomy

1. In this section, you compared vertebrate forelimbs (p. 152). The similarity between the bones in all vertebrate forelimbs and a common ancestor shows that today's vertebrates

   _____.

   However, the various vertebrates are adapted to _____.

2. In this section, you also compared the chimpanzee and the human skeletons (p. 155). A contrast in skeletons shows that the posture differences are due to _____.

   _____.

   A contrast in skulls shows that the facial differences are due to _____.

3. In this section, you also compared vertebrate embryos (p. 157). The similarity in the appearance of vertebrate embryos also shows that today's vertebrates _____

   _____.

Molecular Evidence

1. In this section, you used an antigen-antibody reaction to show how closely related certain vertebrates are to humans (p. 158). Two closely related organisms share _____

   _____.

Laboratory Review 12

1. List three types of evidence that suggest that various types of organisms are related through common descent. _____

2. Why would you expect a fossil buried millions of years ago to not look exactly like a modern-day organism? _____

3. What accounts for many of the skeletal difference between chimpanzees and humans?_____

_____

4. If a characteristic is found in bacteria, fungi, pine trees, snakes, and humans, when did it most likely evolve? _____ Why? _____

_____

5. What are homologous structures, and what do they show about relatedness? _____

_____

6. The development of reptiles, chicks, and humans shows similarities. What can we learn from this observation?_____

7. What do DNA mutations have to do with amino acid changes in a protein? _____

_____

8. How did antigen-antibody reactions help determine the degree of relatedness between species in this laboratory? _____

_____

9. Using plus (+) symbols, show the amount of reaction you would expect when antibodies against human serum are tested against sera from a pig, monkey, and chimpanzee. _____

_____

10. Define the following types of evidence for evolution:

    fossil _____

    common descent _____

    comparative anatomy _____

    adaptation _____

    molecular _____

24

The Vertebrates

Learning Outcomes

Introduction
- State the characteristics that all chordates have in common.   337–38

24.1 Chordates (Phylum Chordata)
- Use the cross section of a lancelet to point out the common characteristics of all chordates.   338–39

24.2 Vertebrates (Subphylum Vertebrata)
- Name the types of vertebrates, and give an example of an animal in each group.   340
- Identify and locate external and internal structures of a frog.   341–42
- Trace the path of air, food, and urine in a frog, and explain the term *urogenital system*.   343–48

24.3 Comparative Vertebrate Anatomy
- Compare the organ systems (except musculoskeletal) of a frog, perch, pigeon, and pig.   349–50
- Relate aspects of an animal's respiratory system to the animal's environment and to features of the animal's circulatory system.   351–55

Introduction

Vertebrates are **chordates.** All chordates have (1) a dorsal tubular nerve cord; (2) a dorsal supporting rod, called a notochord, at some time in their life history; (3) a postanal tail; and, in chordates that breathe by means of gills, (4) pharyngeal pouches that become gill slits. In terrestrial chordates, these pouches are modified for other purposes.

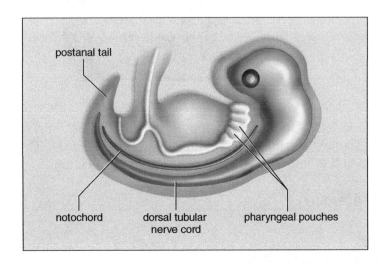

postanal tail

notochord   dorsal tubular   pharyngeal pouches
              nerve cord

In vertebrates, the embryonic notochord is replaced by vertebral column composed of individual vertebrae that protect the nerve cord. The main axis of the internal jointed skeleton consists not only of a vertebral column, but also of a skull that encloses and protects the well-developed brain. There is an extreme degree of cephalization with complex sense organs. The eyes develop as outgrowths of the brain. The ears are primarily equilibrium devices in aquatic vertebrates; and in land vertebrates, they function as sound wave receivers.

The vertebrates are extremely motile and have well-developed muscles and usually paired appendages. They have bilateral symmetry and are segmented, as witnessed by the vertebral column. There is a large coelom, a complete gut, and the circulatory system is closed. They have an efficient means of extracting oxygen from water (gills) or air (lungs) as appropriate. The kidneys are important excretory and water-regulating organs that conserve or rid the body's water as necessary. The sexes are generally separate, and reproduction is usually sexual.

24.1 Chordates (Phylum Chordata)

Among the chordates, two major groups contain invertebrates, and the other contains the vertebrates.

Invertebrate Chordates

The two types of invertebrate chordates are urochordates and cephalochordates.

1. **Urochordates.** The tunicates, or sea squirts (Fig. 24.1), come in varying sizes and shapes, but all have incurrent and excurrent siphons. **Gill slits** are the only remaining chordate characteristic in adult tunicates. Examine any examples of tunicates on display.

Figure 24.1 Urochordates.
The gill slits of a tunicate are the only chordate characteristics remaining in the adult.

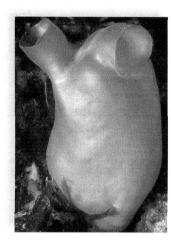 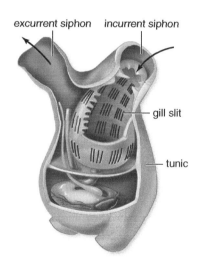

2. **Cephalochordates.** Lancelets, also known as amphioxus *(Branchiostoma),* are small, fishlike animals that occur in shallow marine waters in most parts of the world. They spend most of their time buried in the sandy bottom, with only the anterior end projecting.

Observation: Lancelet Anatomy

Preserved Specimen
1. Examine a preserved lancelet (Fig. 24.2).
2. Identify the **caudal fin** (enlarged tail) used in locomotion, the **dorsal fin,** and the short **ventral fin.**
3. Examine the lancelet's V-shaped muscles.

Figure 24.2 Anatomy of the lancelet, *Branchiostoma*.

Lancelets feed on microscopic particles filtered out of the constant stream of water that enters the mouth and exits through the gill slits into an atrium that opens at the atriopore.

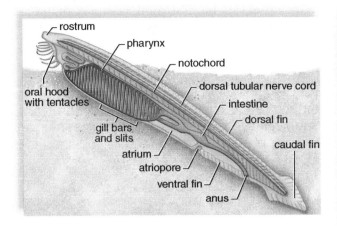

4. Find the tentacled **oral hood,** located anterior to the mouth and covering a vestibule. Water entering the mouth is channeled into the **pharynx,** where food particles are trapped before the water exits at the **atriopore.** Lancelets are filter feeders. Has cephalization occurred? _____

   Explain. _____

   _____

Prepared Slide

Examine a prepared cross section of a lancelet (Fig. 24.3), and note the three chordate characteristics: notochord, dorsal tubular nerve cord, and gill slits.

Figure 24.3 Lancelet cross section.

Cross-section slide as it would appear under a microscope.

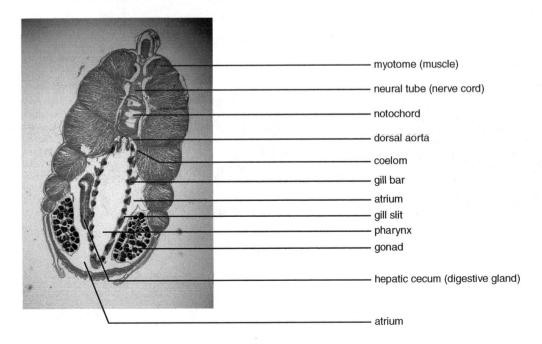

24.2 Vertebrates (Subphylum Vertebrata)

Like arthropods, **vertebrates** are segmented, and specialization of parts has occurred. Arthropods have an exoskeleton, while vertebrates have an endoskeleton, but they both have jointed appendages. In vertebrates, two pairs of appendages are characteristic. The vertebrate brain is more complex than that of arthropods and is enclosed by a skull. Among vertebrates, a high degree of cephalization is the rule. All organ systems are present and efficient.

Diversity of Vertebrates

Like arthropods, there are both aquatic and terrestrial vertebrates (as shown in Fig. 24.4). Fishes are aquatic; adult amphibians may be terrestrial, but most must return to an aquatic habitat to reproduce; and reptiles are terrestrial, although some reptiles, such as sea turtles, are secondarily adapted to life in the water. Mammals are adapted to a wide variety of habitats, including air (e.g., bats), sea (e.g., whales), and land (e.g., humans).

Figure 24.4 Vertebrate groups.

Blue shark

Cartilaginous fishes
Lack operculum and swim bladder; tail fin usually asymmetrical: (sharks, skates, and rays)

Blueback butterflyfish

Bony fishes
Operculum; swim bladder or lungs; tail fin usually symmetrical: lung-fishes, lobe-finned fishes, and ray-finned fishes (herring, salmon, sturgeon, eels, and sea horse)

Northern leopard frog

Amphibians
Tetrapods with nonamniotic egg; nonscaly skin; some show metamorphosis; three-chambered heart; ectothermic: urodeles (salamanders and newts) and anurans (frogs and toads)

Pearl River redbelly turtle

Reptiles
Tetrapods with amniotic egg; scaly skin; ectothermic; squamata (snakes and lizards) and chelonnians (turtles and tortoises)

Scissor-tailed flycatcher

Birds
Now grouped with reptiles; tetrapods with feathers; bipedal with wings; double circulation; endothermic: (sparrows, penguins, and ostriches)

Grey fox

Mammals
Tetrapods with hair, mammary glands; double circulation; endothermic; teeth differentiated: monotremes (spiny anteater and duckbill platypus), marsupials (opossum and kangaroo), and placental mammals (whales, rodents, dogs, cats, elephants, horses, bats, and humans)

Anatomy of the Frog

Frogs are amphibians, a group of animals in which metamorphosis occurs. Metamorphosis includes a change in structure, as when an aquatic tadpole becomes a frog with lungs and limbs (Fig. 24.5). Amphibians were the first vertebrates to be adapted to living on land; however, they typically return to the water to reproduce. Underline every structure mentioned in the following Observation that represents an adaptation to a land environment.

Observation: External Anatomy of the Frog

1. Place a preserved frog *(Rana pipiens)* in a dissecting tray.
2. Identify the bulging eyes, which have a nonmovable upper and lower lid but can be covered by a **nictitating membrane** that serves to moisten the eye.
3. Locate the **tympanum** behind each eye (Fig. 24.5). What is the function of a tympanum? _____

   _____
4. Examine the external **nares** (sing., **naris,** or **nostril**). Insert a probe into an external naris, and observe that it protrudes from one of the paired small openings, the internal nares (Fig. 24.6),

   inside the mouth cavity. What is the function of the nares? _____
5. Identify the paired limbs. The bones of the fore- and hindlimbs are the same as in all tetrapods, in that the first bone articulates with a girdle and the limb ends in phalanges. The hind feet have five

   phalanges, and the forefeet have only four phalanges. Which pair of limbs is longest? _____

   How does a frog locomote on land? _____

   _____

   What is a frog's means of locomotion in the water? _____

   _____

Figure 24.5 External frog anatomy.

Observation: Internal Anatomy of the Frog

Mouth

1. Open your frog's mouth very wide (Fig. 24.6), cutting the angles of the jaws if necessary.
2. Identify the tongue attached to the lower jaw's anterior end.
3. Find the **auditory (eustachian) tube** opening in the angle of the jaws. These tubes lead to the ears. Auditory tubes equalize air pressure in the ears.
4. Examine the **maxillary teeth** located along the rim of the upper jaw. Another set of teeth—**vomerine teeth**—is present just behind the midportion of the upper jaw.
5. Locate the **glottis,** a slit through which air passes into and out of the **trachea,** the short tube from glottis to lungs. What is the function of a glottis? _____

   _____

6. Identify the **esophagus,** which lies dorsal and posterior to the glottis and leads to the stomach.

Figure 24.6   Mouth cavity of a frog.
a. Drawing. **b.** Dissected specimen.

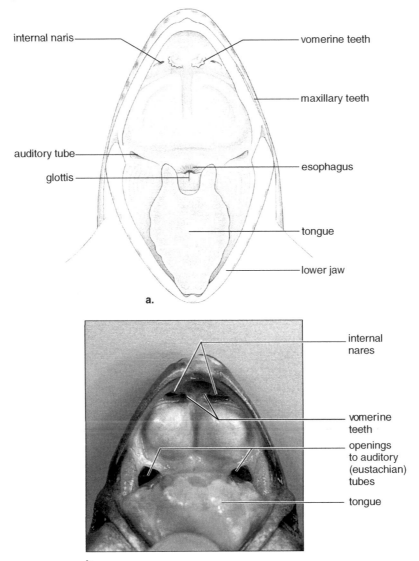

Opening the Frog

1. Place the frog ventral side up in the dissecting pan. Lift the skin with forceps, and use scissors to make a large, circular cut to remove the skin from the abdominal region as close to the limbs as possible. Cut only skin, not muscle.
2. Now, remove the muscles by cutting through them in the same circular fashion. At the same time, cut through any bones you encounter. A vein, called the abdominal vein, will be slightly attached to the internal side of the muscles.
3. Identify the **coelom,** or body cavity.
4. If your frog is female, the abdominal cavity is likely to be filled by a pair of large, transparent **ovaries,** each containing hundreds of black and white eggs. Gently lift the left ovary with forceps, and find its place of attachment. Cut through the attachment, and remove the ovary in one piece.

Respiratory System and Liver

1. Insert a probe into the glottis, and observe its passage into the trachea. Enlarge the glottis by making short cuts above and below it. When the glottis is spread open, you will see a fold on either side; these are the vocal cords used in croaking.
2. Identify the **lungs,** two small sacs on either side of the midline and partially hidden under the liver (Fig. 24.7). Trace the path of air from the external nares to the lungs. _____

_____

3. Locate the **liver,** the large, prominent, dark-brown organ in the midventral portion of the trunk (Fig. 24.7). Between the right half and left half of the liver, find the **gallbladder.**

Circulatory System

1. Lift the liver gently. Identify the **heart,** covered by a membranous covering (the **pericardium**). With forceps, lift the covering, and gently slit it open. The heart consists of a single, thick-walled **ventricle** and two (right and left) anterior, thin-walled **atria.**
2. Locate the three large veins that join together beneath the heart to form the **sinus venosus.** (To lift the heart, you may have to snip the slender strand of tissue that connects the atria to the pericardium.) Blood from the sinus venosus enters the right atrium. The left atrium receives blood from the lungs.
3. Find the **conus arteriosus,** a single, wide arterial vessel leaving the ventricle and passing ventrally over the right atrium. Follow the conus arteriosus forward to where it divides into three branches on each side. The middle artery on each side is the **systemic artery,** which fuses behind the heart to become the **dorsal aorta.** The dorsal aorta transports blood through the body cavity and gives off many branches. The **posterior vena cava** begins between the two kidneys and returns blood to the sinus venosus. Which vessel lies above (dorsal to) the other? _____

_____

Digestive Tract

1. Identify the **esophagus,** a very short connection between the mouth and the stomach. Lift the left liver lobe, and identify the stomach, whitish and J-shaped. The **stomach** connects with the esophagus anteriorly and with the small intestine posteriorly.
2. Find the **small intestine** and the **large intestine,** which enters the **cloaca.** The cloaca lies beneath the pubic bone and is a general receptacle for the intestine, the reproductive system, and the urinary system. It opens to the outside by way of the anus. Trace the path of food in the digestive tract from the mouth to the cloaca. _____

_____

Accessory Glands

1. You identified the liver and gallbladder previously. Now try to find the **pancreas,** a yellowish tissue near the stomach and intestine.
2. Locate the **spleen,** a small, pea-shaped body near the stomach.

Figure 24.7 Internal organs of a female frog, ventral view.

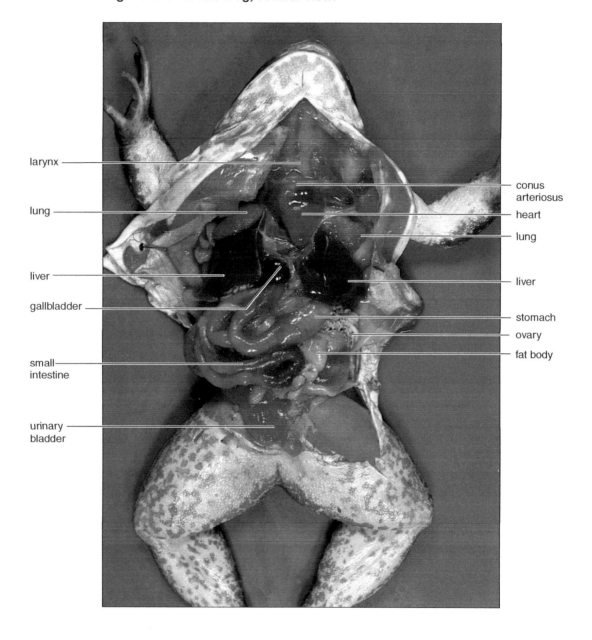

larynx

lung

liver

gallbladder

small intestine

urinary bladder

conus arteriosus

heart

lung

liver

stomach

ovary

fat body

Urogenital System

1. Identify the **kidneys,** long, narrow organs lying against the dorsal body wall (Fig. 24.8).
2. Locate the **testes** in a male frog (Fig. 24.8). Testes are yellow, oval organs attached to the anterior portions of the kidneys. Several small ducts, the **vasa efferentia,** carry sperm into kidney ducts that also carry urine from the kidneys. **Fat bodies,** which store fat, are attached to the testes.
3. Locate the ovaries in a female frog. The ovaries are attached to the dorsal body wall (Fig. 24.9). Fat bodies are also attached to the ovaries. Highly coiled **oviducts** lead to the cloaca. The ostium (opening) of the oviduct is dorsal to the liver.
4. Find the **mesonephric ducts**—thin, white tubes that carry urine from the kidney to the cloaca. In female frogs, you will have to remove the left ovary to see the mesonephric ducts.
5. Locate the **cloaca.** You will need to split through the bones of the pelvic girdle in the midventral line and carefully separate the bones and muscles to find the cloaca.
6. Identify the urinary bladder attached to the ventral wall of the cloaca. In frogs, urine backs up into the bladder from the cloaca.
7. Explain the term *urogenital system.* _____

_____

8. The cloaca receives material from (1) _____ ,
   (2) _____ , and (3) _____ .
9. Compare the frog's urogenital system to the human urinary system, which in females has no connection to the genital system. Beside each organ listed on the right tell how the comparable frog organ differs from that of a human.

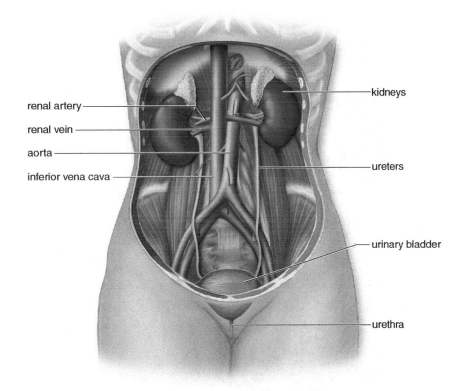

renal artery
renal vein
aorta
inferior vena cava

kidneys
ureters
urinary bladder
urethra

Figure 24.8 Urogenital system of a male frog.

a. Drawing. **b.** Dissected specimen.

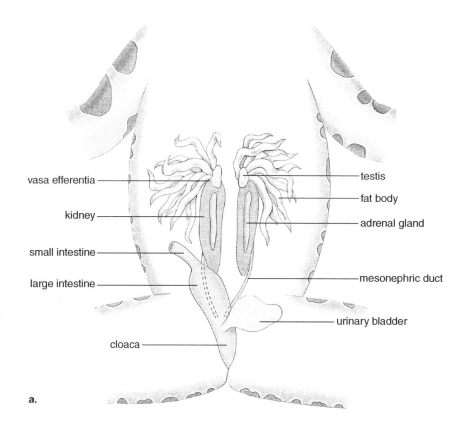

vasa efferentia

kidney

small intestine

large intestine

cloaca

testis

fat body

adrenal gland

mesonephric duct

urinary bladder

a.

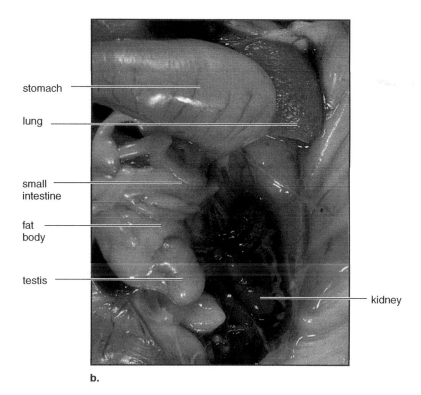

stomach

lung

small intestine

fat body

testis

kidney

b.

**Figure 24.9 Urogenital system
of a female frog.**
a. Drawing. b. Dissected specimen.

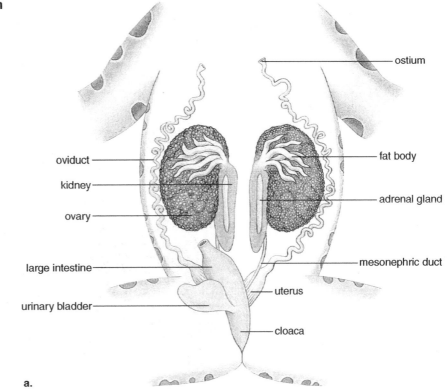

ostium

oviduct

kidney

ovary

large intestine

urinary bladder

fat body

adrenal gland

mesonephric duct

uterus

cloaca

a.

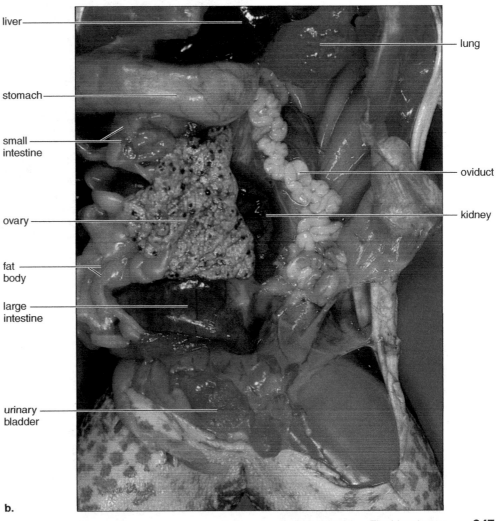

liver

stomach

small
intestine

ovary

fat
body

large
intestine

urinary
bladder

lung

oviduct

kidney

b.

Nervous System

In the frog demonstration dissection, identify the **brain,** lying exposed within the skull. With the help of Figure 24.10, find the major parts of the brain.

Figure 24.10   Frog brain, dorsal view.
a. Drawing. **b.** Dissected specimen.

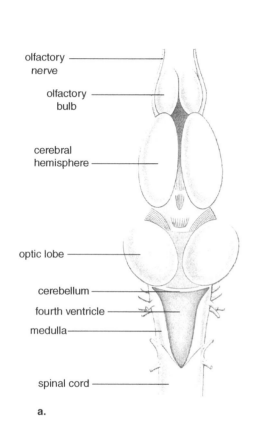

olfactory nerve

olfactory bulb

cerebral hemisphere

optic lobe

cerebellum

fourth ventricle

medulla

spinal cord

a.

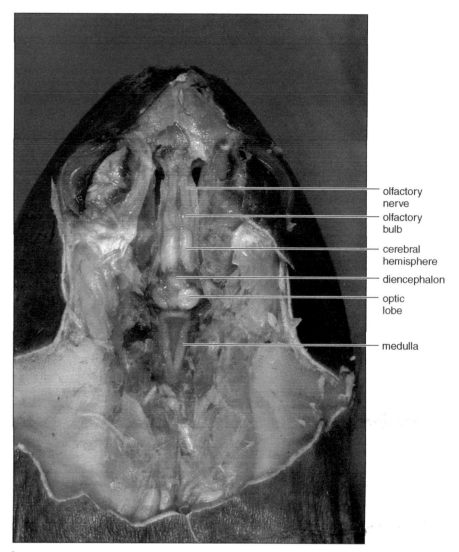

olfactory nerve

olfactory bulb

cerebral hemisphere

diencephalon

optic lobe

medulla

b.

24.3 Comparative Vertebrate Anatomy

Examine the frog (amphibian), perch (fish), pigeon (reptile), and pig (mammal) on display.

Observation: External Anatomy of Vertebrates

1. Compare the external features of the frog, perch, pigeon, and pig by answering the following questions and recording your observations in Table 24.1.
   a. Is the skin smooth, scaly, hairy, or feathery?
   b. Is there any external evidence of segmentation?
   c. Are all forms bilaterally symmetrical?
   d. Is the body differentiated into regions?
   e. Is there a well-defined neck?
   f. Is there a postanal tail?
   g. Are there nares?
   h. Is there a cloaca, or are the urogenital and anal openings separate?
   i. Are eyelids present? How many?
   j. Is there external evidence of an ear?
   k. How many appendages are there? (Fins are considered appendages.) (Fig. 24.11)
   l. How many digits are there in the forelimb?
   m. How many digits are there in the hindlimb?
   n. Are nails or claws present?

Table 24.1 Comparison of External Features				
	Frog	**Perch**	**Pigeon**	**Pig**
a. Skin				
b. Segmentation				
c. Symmetry				
d. Regions				
e. Neck				
f. Postanal tail				
g. Nares				
h. Cloaca				
i. Eyelids				
j. External ears				
k. Appendages				
l. Digits in forelimb				
m. Digits in hindlimb				
n. Nails or claws				

2. Evidence that birds are reptiles: Birds

    a. have feathers, which are modified scales.

    b. have scales on their feet.

    c. and reptiles both lay eggs.

    d. and reptiles have similar internal organs.

    e. and reptiles also show some skeletal (skull) similarities.

Which of these can you substantiate by external examination? _____

_____

3. The perch, pigeon, and pig have a nearly impenetrable covering. Why is this an advantage in

each case? _____

_____

4. A frog uses its skin for breathing. Describe its skin in more detail.

_____

Figure 24.11   Perch anatomy.

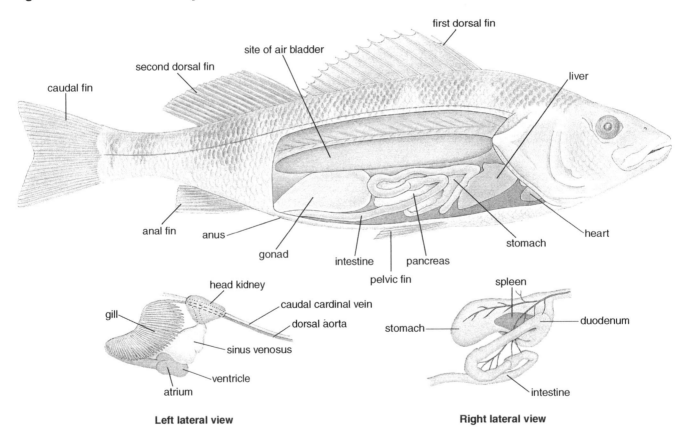

Left lateral view   Right lateral view

Figure 24.12 Cardiovascular systems in vertebrates.

a. In a fish, the blood moves in a single loop. The heart has a single atrium and ventricle, which pumps the blood into the gill region, where gas exchange takes place. **b.** Amphibians have a double-loop system in which the heart pumps blood to both the gills and the body. **c.** In birds and mammals, the right side pumps blood to the lungs, and the left side pumps blood to the body.

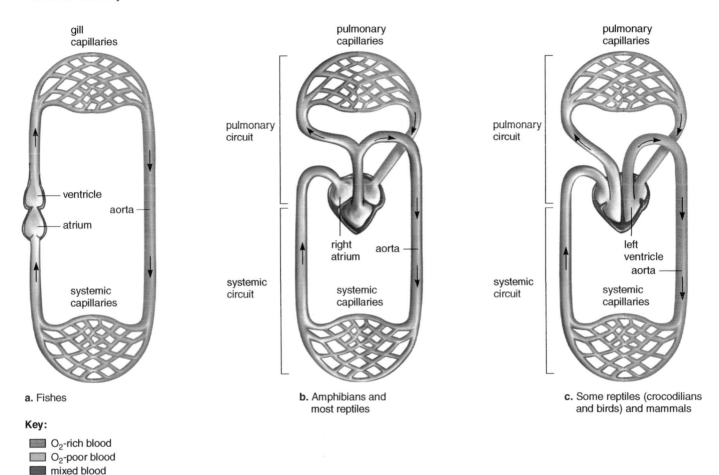

a. Fishes

b. Amphibians and most reptiles

c. Some reptiles (crocodilians and birds) and mammals

Key:

- O_2-rich blood
- O_2-poor blood
- mixed blood

Observation: Internal Anatomy of Vertebrates

1. Examine the internal organs of the frog, perch, pigeon, and pig.
2. If necessary, make a median longitudinal incision in the ventral body wall, from the jaws to the cloaca or anus. The body cavity is a coelom.
3. Which of these animals has a **diaphragm** dividing the body cavity into **thorax** and **abdomen?**

Circulatory Systems

1. Study heart models for a fish, amphibian, bird, and mammal (Fig. 24.12).
2. Trace the path of the vessel that leaves the ventricle(s), and determine whether the animals have a **pulmonary system** (Fig. 24.12). The word *pulmonary* comes from the Latin *pulmonarius,* meaning "lungs." A pulmonary system contrasts with a **branchial system,** which involves gills.
3. Locate the **sinus venosus,** which enters the atrium in the perch and frog. In the frog, the sinus venosus is a triangular membranous sac, located just behind the atria and ventricle, that enters the right atrium. The pig and pigeon do not have a sinus venosus.

Figure 24.13   Pigeon anatomy.

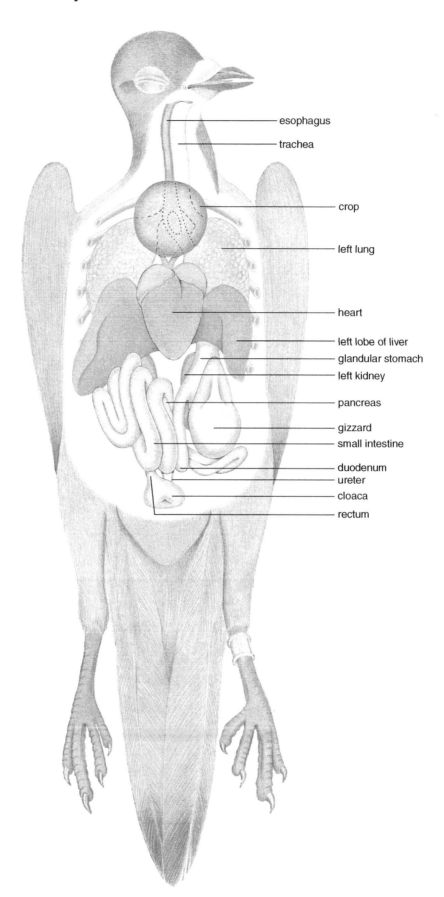

esophagus

trachea

crop

left lung

heart

left lobe of liver

glandular stomach

left kidney

pancreas

gizzard

small intestine

duodenum

ureter

cloaca

rectum

Table 24.2 Comparative Circulatory Systems

Animal	Number of Heart Chambers	Pulmonary System (Yes or No)
Frog		
Perch		
Pigeon		
Pig		

4. Complete Table 24.2.

5. Do fish have a separate circulatory system to the gills? _____

6. Would you expect blood pressure to be high or low after blood has moved through the gills? _____

7. What animals studied have a separate circulatory system for the respiratory organ? _____

8. What is the advantage of having a separate circulatory system that returns blood to the heart? _____

_____

9. Which of these animals have a four-chambered heart? _____

10. What is the advantage of having separate ventricles? _____

_____

11. Contrast the body temperature of animals having a four-chambered heart to that of animals not

having a four-chambered heart. Comment. _____

_____

_____

Respiratory Systems

1. Compare the respiratory systems of the frog, perch, pigeon, and pig (Figs. 24.7, 24.11, 24.13, and 24.14), and complete Table 24.3 (see page 354) by checking the anatomical features that appear in each animal.

2. On the basis of your examination, contrast the respiratory system of the perch with those of the

other animals. _____

_____

Can the differences be related to the environment of the perch compared to the environment of the

other animals? _____ Explain. _____

_____

3. What anatomical feature is present in the pig and pigeon but missing in the frog? _____

_____

Can this difference be related to the fact that frogs breathe by positive pressure, while birds and

mammals breathe by negative pressure? _____ (A frog swallows air and then pushes the air

into its lungs; in birds and mammals, the thorax expands first, and then the air is drawn in.)

Explain. _____

_____

_____

4. What anatomical feature is present only in birds? _____ This feature allows the air to pass one way through the lungs of a bird and greatly increases the bird's ability to extract oxygen from the air.

5. What anatomical feature is present only in mammals? _____
Of what benefit is this feature to mammals? _____

_____

Table 24.3 Respiratory Systems						
	Glottis	Larynx	Trachea	Lungs	Rib Cage*	Diaphragm	Air Sacs
Frog							
Perch							
Pigeon							
Pig							

*A rib cage consists of ribs plus a sternum. Some ribs are connected to the sternum, which lies at the midline in the anterior portion of the rib cage.

Digestive Systems

Figures 24.7, 24.11, 24.13, and 24.14 show the digestive systems of the animals you are studying.

1. Locate the stomach, small intestine, large intestine, rectum, and anus.
2. Is the position of the pancreas the same in all specimens? _____
3. Locate the liver.
4. Is a gallbladder present in all specimens? _____ Explain. _____

_____

5. Is a spleen present in all specimens? _____ Does it have the same location in all cases? _____

_____

Urogenital Systems

1. Identify the gonads and kidneys in the animals you are studying.
2. Try to trace their ducts to the urogenital sinus or cloaca, and check your previous external features observation (see Table 24.1) as to whether a cloaca is present. The urogenital system of the frog is described in the Observation: Internal Anatomy of Frog.

Figure 24.14 Fetal pig anatomy.

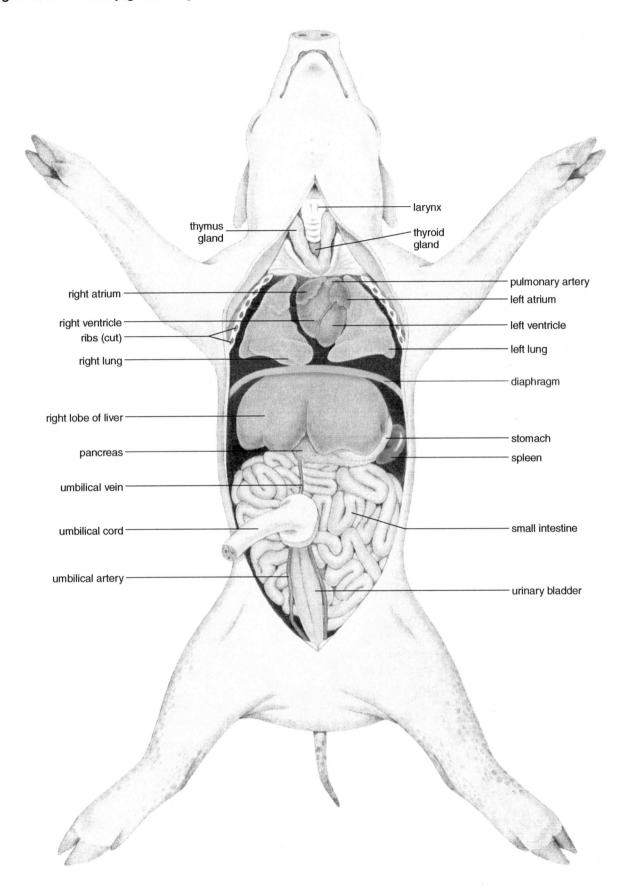

larynx

thymus gland

thyroid gland

right atrium

pulmonary artery

left atrium

right ventricle

ribs (cut)

left ventricle

right lung

left lung

diaphragm

right lobe of liver

stomach

pancreas

spleen

umbilical vein

umbilical cord

small intestine

umbilical artery

urinary bladder

Laboratory Review 24

1. What are the four characteristics of all chordates?

   a. _____

   b. _____

   c. _____

   d. _____

2. Why isn't a lancelet a vertebrate? _____

   _____

3. Which groups of vertebrates are fully adapted to life on land?

   _____

4. Complete each of the following sentences: In a frog, . . .

   a. the glottis allows air to enter the _____

   b. the esophagus allows food to enter the _____

   c. the cloaca receives material from the _____ , _____ , and _____

   d. sperm reach the cloaca by way of the _____

5. What is the major difference between the heart of a frog and that of a pig? _____

   _____

6. A pulmonary circuit is seen in vertebrate animals adapted to life on land. Explain. _____

   _____

7. What is the major difference between the respiratory system of a perch and that of a frog, a pigeon, and a pig? _____

A

Preparing a Laboratory Report/ Laboratory Report Form

A laboratory report has the sections (and paragraphs) noted in the outline that follows. Use this description and a copy of the worksheet provided on page 521 to help you write a report assigned by your instructor.

1. **Introduction:**   Tell the reader what the experiment was about.
   a. **Background information:**   Begin by giving an overview of the topic.
      Look at the Introduction to the laboratory (and/or at the introduction to the section for which you are writing the report). *Do not copy the information,* but use it to indicate ideas about what information to include. For example, suppose you are doing a laboratory report on "Solar Energy" in Laboratory 6 (Photosynthesis). You might want to give a definition of photosynthesis and explain the composition of white light.
   b. **Purpose:**   Next, state what the experiment was about.
      Think about the steps of the experiment, and then decide what its purpose was. Since you tested the effect of white and green light on photosynthesis, you might state that the purpose of this experiment was to determine the effect of white light versus green light on the photosynthetic rate.
   c. **Hypothesis:**   Finally, state what results you expected from the experiment.
      Most likely, the Introduction to the laboratory (and/or the particular section) will hint at the expected results. State this in the form of a hypothesis. For example, you might hypothesize that white light would be more effective for photosynthesis than green light.
2. **Procedure:**   Tell the reader how you did the experiment.
   a. **Equipment used:**   Help the reader envision the experimental setup.
      Look at any illustrations that accompany the experiment. For example, look at Figure 6.4, and read the Experimental Procedure, which describes how the experiment is conducted. Now, describe the equipment in your own words. You might state that a 150-watt lamp was the source of white light directed at *Elodea* placed in a test tube filled with a solution of sodium bicarbonate ($NaHCO_3$). A beaker of water placed between the lamp and test tube was a heat absorber.
   b. **Collection of data:**   Tell the reader how the experiment was done.
      Think about what you did during the experiment. What did you observe, or what did you measure? You might state that the rate of photosynthesis was determined by the amount of oxygen released and was measured by how far water moved in a side arm of the test tube.

3. **Results:** Present the data in a clear manner.
   a. **Graph or table:** If at all possible, show your data in a graph or table. Look at any tables you filled in during the experiment, and reproduce those sections that pertain to data collection. (Do not include any columns that have to do with interpretation.) To continue with the Laboratory 6 example, you could reproduce Tables 6.2 and 6.3. You also might be able to draw a graph depicting results. For example, the results recorded in Table 5.2 might look like the graph at right.

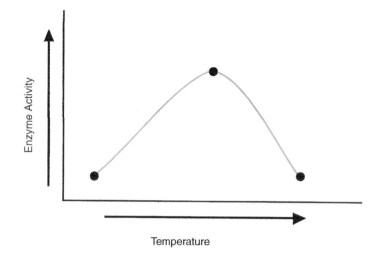

   b. **Description of data:** Examine your data, and decide what they tell you. For Table 6.3, you might state that the data in the table indicate that the rate of photosynthesis with white light was faster than with green light.
4. **Discussion:** Interpret your data and offer conclusions.
   a. **Support of hypothesis:** Tell whether the hypothesis was supported. Compare your hypothesis with your data. Do your data agree with the hypothesis? You might state that your results supported the hypothesis that white light gives a higher rate of photosynthesis than green light.
   b. **Explanation:** Explain why you think you got the results you did. Look at any questions you answered while in the laboratory, and use them to help you decide on an appropriate explanation. For example, the answers to the questions in Solar Energy section 6.2 might help you state that white light gives a higher rate of photosynthesis because it contains all the visual light rays. Green light gives a lower rate of photosynthesis because green plants do not absorb green light. (Be sure to report your data exactly. If your results fail to support the hypothesis, explain why you think this occurred.)
   c. **Conclusion:** Review the entire experiment in your mind, and then explain what you learned. You might state that you learned that the quality of light can affect the rate of photosynthesis.

POINTS TO REMEMBER

1. *Clarity.* Your report should be organized and presented so that the reader can easily understand your work.
2. *Good writing.* Pay particular attention to grammar and style. Your writing will be enhanced by careful proofreading and revision. Have someone else read and critique a draft of your report. Then consider his or her comments seriously in your revisions.
3. *Observations and interpretations.* Keep the distinction between observations and interpretations clear. These are frequently confused in student reports.
4. *Exercise good judgment.* As you prepare your report, you will constantly make difficult decisions about how best to present and interpret your data. Your attention to these decisions will be reflected in the quality of your report.

Laboratory Report for _____

1. Introduction
    a. Background information

    b. Purpose

    c. Hypothesis

2. Procedure
    a. Equipment used

    b. Collection of data

3. Results
    a. Graph or table
      (Place these on attached sheets.)

    b. Description of data

4. Discussion
    a. Support of hypothesis

    b. Explanation

    c. Conclusion

B

Metric System

Unit and Abbreviation	Metric Equivalent	Approximate English-to-Metric Equivalents	Units of Temperature

Length

nanometer (nm)	$= 10^{-9}$ m (10^{-3} μm)
micrometer (μm)	$= 10^{-6}$ m (10^{-3} mm)
millimeter (mm)	$= 0.001$ (10^{-3}) m
centimeter (cm)	$= 0.01$ (10^{-2}) m
meter (m)	$= 100$ (10^2) cm
	$= 1,000$ mm
kilometer (km)	$= 1,000$ (10^3) m

1 inch	$= 2.54$ cm
1 foot	$= 30.5$ cm
1 foot	$= 0.30$ m
1 yard	$= 0.91$ m
1 mi	$= 1.6$ km

Weight (mass)

nanogram (ng)	$= 10^{-9}$ g
microgram (μg)	$= 10^{-6}$ g
milligram (mg)	$= 10^{-3}$ g
gram (g)	$= 1,000$ mg
kilogram (kg)	$= 1,000$ (10^3) g
metric ton (t)	$= 1,000$ kg

1 ounce	$= 28.3$ g
1 pound	$= 454$ g
	$= 0.45$ kg
1 ton	$= 0.91$ t

Volume

microliter (μl)	$= 10^{-6}$ l (10^{-3} ml)
milliliter (ml)	$= 10^{-3}$ liter
	$= 1$ cm³ (cc)
	$= 1,000$ mm³
liter (l)	$= 1,000$ ml
kiloliter (kl)	$= 1,000$ liter

1 tsp	$= 5$ ml
1 fl oz	$= 30$ ml
1 pint	$= 0.47$ liter
1 quart	$= 0.95$ liter
1 gallon	$= 3.79$ liter

Common Temperatures

°C	°F	
100	212	Water boils at standard temperature and pressure.
71	160	Flash pasteurization of milk
57	134	Highest recorded temperature in the United States, Death Valley, July 10, 1913
41	105.8	Average body temperature of a marathon runner in hot weather
37	98.6	Human body temperature
13.7	56.66	Human survival is still possible at this temperature.
0	32.0	Water freezes at standard temperature and pressure.

°F / °C thermometer scale:

212° — 210 / 100 — 100°
160° — 160 / 70 — 71°
134° — / 57°
131° — 130 /
105.8° — / 40 — 41°
98.6° — 100 / 37°
56.66° — 60 / 13.7°
32° — 30 / 0 — 0°

To convert temperature scales:

$$°C = \frac{(°F - 32)}{1.8}$$

$$°F = 1.8°C + 32$$

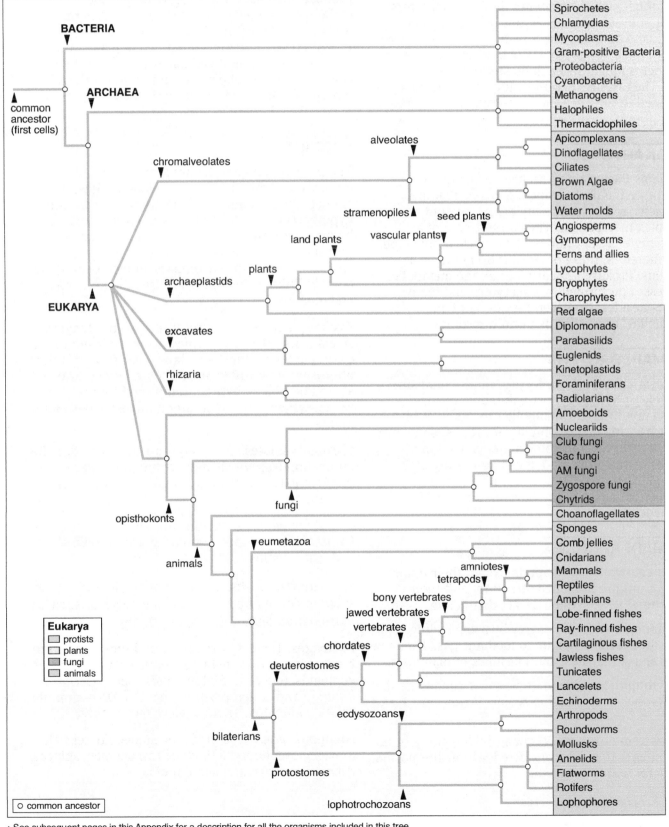

BACTERIA

ARCHAEA

common
ancestor
(first cells)

chromalveolates

alveolates

stramenopiles

seed plants
vascular plants
land plants
plants
archaeplastids

excavates

rhizaria

EUKARYA

opisthokonts

fungi

animals

eumetazoa

amniotes
tetrapods
bony vertebrates
jawed vertebrates
vertebrates
chordates
deuterostomes

ecdysozoans

bilaterians

protostomes

lophotrochozoans

Spirochetes
Chlamydias
Mycoplasmas
Gram-positive Bacteria
Proteobacteria
Cyanobacteria
Methanogens
Halophiles
Thermacidophiles
Apicomplexans
Dinoflagellates
Ciliates
Brown Algae
Diatoms
Water molds
Angiosperms
Gymnosperms
Ferns and allies
Lycophytes
Bryophytes
Charophytes
Red algae
Diplomonads
Parabasilids
Euglenids
Kinetoplastids
Foraminiferans
Radiolarians
Amoeboids
Nucleariids
Club fungi
Sac fungi
AM fungi
Zygospore fungi
Chytrids
Choanoflagellates
Sponges
Comb jellies
Cnidarians
Mammals
Reptiles
Amphibians
Lobe-finned fishes
Ray-finned fishes
Cartilaginous fishes
Jawless fishes
Tunicates
Lancelets
Echinoderms
Arthropods
Roundworms
Mollusks
Annelids
Flatworms
Rotifers
Lophophores

Eukarya
☐ protists
☐ plants
☐ fungi
☐ animals

○ common ancestor

* See subsequent pages in this Appendix for a description for all the organisms included in this tree.

Tree of Life

The Tree of Life depicted in this appendix is based on the phylogenetic (evolutionary) trees presented in the text. Figure 1.5 showed how the three domains of life—Bacteria, Archaea, and Eukarya—are related. This relationship is also apparent in the Tree of Life, which combines the individual trees given in the text for eukaryotic protists, plants, fungi, and animals. In combining these trees, we show how all organisms may be related to one another through the evolutionary process.

The text also described the organisms that are included in the tree. These descriptions are repeated here.

PROKARYOTES

Domains Bacteria and Archaea (Chapter 20) constitute the prokaryotic organisms that are characterized by their simple structure but a complex metabolism. The chromosome of a prokaryote is not bounded by a nuclear envelope, and therefore, these organisms do not have a nucleus. Prokaryotes carry out all the metabolic processes performed by eukaryotes and many others besides. However, they do not have organelles, except for plentiful ribosomes.

DOMAIN BACTERIA

Bacteria are the most plentiful of all organisms, capable of living in most habitats, and carry out many different metabolic processes. While most bacteria are aerobic heterotrophs, some are photosynthetic, and some are chemosynthetic. Motile forms move by flagella consisting of a single filament. Their cell wall contains peptidoglycan and they have distinctive RNA sequences.

DOMAIN ARCHAEA

Their cell walls lack peptidoglycan, their lipids have a unique branched structure, and their ribosomal RNA sequences are distinctive.

Methanogens. Obtain energy by using hydrogen gas to reduce carbon dioxide to methane gas. They live in swamps, marshes, and intestines of mammals.

Extremophiles. Able to grow under conditions that are too hot, too cold, and too acidic for most forms of life to survive.

Nonextreme archaea. Grow in wide variety of environments that are considered within the normal range for living organisms.

DOMAIN EUKARYA

Eukarya have a complex cell structure with a nucleus and several types of organelles that compartmentalize the cell. Mitochondria that produce ATP and chloroplasts that produce carbohydrate are derived from prokaryotes that took up residence in a larger nucleated cell. Protists tend to be unicellular, while plants, fungi, and animals are multicellular with specialized cells. Each multicellular group is characterized by a particular mode of nutrition. Flagella, if present, have a 9 + 2 organization.

PROTISTS

The protists (Chapter 21) are a catchall group for any eukaryote that is not a plant, fungus, or animal. Division into six supergroups is a working hypothesis that is subject to change as more is known about the evolutionary relationships of the protists. A supergroup is a major eukaryotic group and six supergroups encompass all members of the domain Eukarya including protists, plants, fungi, and animals.

Archaeplastids. A supergroup of photosynthesizers with plastids derived from endosymbiotic cyanobacteria. Includes land plants and other photosynthetic organisms, such as green and red algae and charophytes, exemplified by the stoneworts, which share a common ancestor with land plants.

Chromalveolates. A supergroup that includes the Stramenopiles, which have a unique flagella, and the Alveolates, which have small sacs under plasma membrane.

Stramenopiles. Includes brown algae, such as *Laminaria* and *Fucus*, diatoms, golden brown algae, and water molds.

Alveolates. Includes dinoflagellates, ciliates such as *Paramecium*, and apicomplexans, such as *Plasmodium vivax*.

Excavates. Have an excavated oral grove and form a supergroup that includes zooflagellates, such as euglenids (e.g.,); diplomonads, such as *Giardia lambia;* and kinetoplastids (have a DNA granule called a kinetoplast), such as trypanosomes.

Amoebozoans. Supergroup of amoeboid cells that move by pseudopodia. Includes amoeboids, such as *Amoeba proteus,* and slime molds.

Rhizarians. Supergroup of amoeboid cells with tests. They form a supergroup that includes the foraminiferans and the radiolarians.

Opisthokonts. Supergroup named for members that have a single posterior flagellum (Gk., *opistho,* rear and *kontos,* pole). Includes animals and choanoflagellates that may be related to the common ancestor of animals and the fungi.

PLANTS

Plants (Chapter 23) are photosynthetic eukaryotes that became adapted to living on land. Includes aquatic green algae called charophytes, which have a haploid life cycle and share certain traits with the land plants.

Land Plants (embryophytes)

Have an alternation of generation life cycle; protect a multicellular sporophyte embryo; produce gametes in gametangia; possess apical tissue that produces complex tissues; and a waxy cuticle that prevents water loss.

Bryophytes. Low-lying, nonvascular plants that prefer moist locations: the dominant gametophyte produces flagellated sperm. The dependent sporophyte is unbranched and produces windblown spores. Includes mosses, liverworts, and hornworts.

Vascular Plants

Have a dominant, branched sporophyte with vascular tissue: a lignified xylem that transports water, and phloem that transports organic nutrients. Typically produces roots, stems, and leaves; the gametophyte is eventually dependent on the sporophyte.

Lycophytes (club mosses). Have leaves called microphylls, which have a single, unbranched vein. The sporangia, which are borne on sides of leaves, produce windblown spores. The independent and separate gametophyte produces flagellated sperm.

Ferns and their allies. Have leaves called megaphylls that have branched veins. The dominant sporophyte produces windblown spores in sporangia borne on leaves, and the independent and separate gametophyte produces flagellated sperm. Includes ferns, whisk ferns, and horsetails, see pages 417-418.

Seed Plants

Have leaves that are megaphylls; a dominant sporophyte produces heterospores that become dependent male and female gametophytes.

Male gametophyte is pollen grain and female gametophyte develops within ovule, which becomes a seed.

Gymnosperms. Large, cone-bearing trees. The sporophyte bears pollen cones, which produce wind-blown pollen (male gametophyte), and seed cones, which bear ovules. Ovules develop into naked seeds. Includes conifers, gnetophytes, the ginko, and cycads, see pages 420-422.

Angiosperms (flowering plants). Nonwoody or woody plants that live in all habitats. The sporophyte bears flowers, which produce pollen grains, and bears ovules within ovary. Following double fertilization, ovules become seeds that enclose a sporophyte embryo and endosperm (nutrient tissue). Fruit develops from ovary.

FUNGI

Fungi (Chapter 22) have multicellular bodies composed of hyphae; usually absorb food and lack flagella; and produce nonmotile spores during both asexual and sexual reproduction.

Chytrids (Chytridiomycota). Are aquatic fungi with flagellated spores and gametes.

Zygospore fungi (Zygomycota). Exemplified by black bread mold; produce a thick-walled zygospore during sexual reproduction.

AM fungi (Glomeromycota). Form a mutualistic relationship with plants called mycorrhizae.

Sac fungi (Ascomycota). Exemplified by cup fungi; produce fruiting bodies during sexual reproduction where spores develop in fingerlike sacs called asci.

Club fungi (Basidiomycota). Exemplified by mushrooms; produce fruiting bodies during sexual reproduction where spores develop in club-shaped structures called basidia.

ANIMALS

Animals (Chapters 28 and 29) are multicellular, usually with specialized tissues and digestive cavity; ingest or absorb food; and have a diploid life cycle.

Sponges. Have an asymmetrical, saclike body perforated by pores internal cavity lined by food-filtering cells called choanocytes; spicules serve as internal skeleton.

Ctenophores. Have two tentacles; eight rows of cilia that resemble combs; biradial symmetry. Includes comb jellies.

Cnidarians. Radially symmetrical with two tissue layers; sac body plan; and tentacles with nematocysts. Includes hydras, jellyfish, sea anemones, and corals.

Protostomes

Bilaterally symmetrical with protostome development in which the first opening is the mouth.

Lophotrochozoans

Includes lophophores, which have a specific type of ciliated feeding device (see page 516); and trochophores, which have a trochophore larva or their ancestors had one.

Flatworms. Bilaterally symmetrical with cephalization; have three tissue layers and organ systems, including both male and female sex organs. They are acoelomate with an incomplete digestive tract that can be lost in parasites. Planarians are free-living; flukes and tapeworms are parasitic.

Rotifers (aquatic wheel animals). Microscopic aquatic animals with a corona (crown of cilia) that looks like a spinning wheel when in motion.

Annelids. Segmented with body rings and setae. Cephalization occurs in some polychaetes. They utilize the coelom as a hydroskeleton and have a closed circulatory system. Includes earthworms, polychaetes, and leeches.

Molluscs. Have a foot, mantel, and visceral mass. The foot is variously modified; in many, the mantle secretes a calcium carbonate shell. They have a coelom and all organ systems. Includes clams, snails, and squids.

Ecdysozoa

Animals that undergo ecdysis (molting).

Roundworms. Have a pseudocoelom, which they use as a hydroskeleton, and a complete digestive tract. Although many are free-living, parasites such as *Ascaris*, pinworms, hookworms, and filarial worms are well known.

Arthropods. Have a chitinous exoskeleton with jointed appendages, specialized for particular functions. Insects, many of which are winged, are the most numerous of all arthropods and animals. Includes crustaceans, spiders, scorpions, centipedes, and millipedes, in addition to insects.

Deuterostomes

Bilaterally symmetrical with deuterstome development in which the second opening is the mouth.

Echinoderms. Radial symmetry as adults; unique water-vascular system; and associated tube feet. Their endoskeleton is composed of calcium plates. Includes sea stars, sea urchins, sand dollars, and sea cucumbers.

Chordates. Have a notochord, dorsal tubular nerve cord, pharyngeal pouches, and postanal tail at some time; segmentation has led to specialization of parts. Includes tunicates, lancelets, and vertebrates.

Lancelets (Cephalochordates). Marine, nonvertebrate chordates shaped like a lance that retain the four chordate characteristics as an adult. Segmentation of muscles is obvious.

Tunicates (Urochordates). Marine, nonvertebrate chordates that produce a tunic, a tough sac containing mainly cellulose. Only the larva has the characteristics of chordates; the adult has gill slits. Segmentation is not present.

Vertebrates (Vertebrata). Chordates in which the notochord has been replaced with vertebrae. Vertebrae, which make up the spine, are an obvious sign of segmentation.

Fishes. Diverse group of marine or freshwater vertebrates that breathe by means of gills and have a single-looped and closed blood circuit. Vertebral column of bone or cartilage; most have jaws and paired appendages. Includes jawless, cartilaginous, ray-finned, and lobe-finned fishes.

Amphibians. Vertebrates with lungs, cutaneous respiration, and a three-chambered heart. Frogs and salamanders have legs but caecilians do not. Many have gill-breathing larva that undergoes metamorphosis.

Reptiles. Vertebrates fully adapted to living on land because they have an amniotic-shelled egg, dry, scaly skin, and a rib cage. Turtles, lizards, and snakes have a three-chambered heart but crocodiles and alligators have a four-chambered heart. Birds are crocodilians unique among reptiles because they have feathers and are endothermic.

Mammals. Vertebrates characterized by fur and mammary glands. They are endothermic amniotes that, for the most part, practice internal fertilization and development. Monotremes lay shelled eggs; marsupials have a pouch where offspring finish development; and placental mammals produce young capable of independency.

Credits

Index